BERNARD HARTLEY & PETER VINEY

DESTINATIONS

WORKBOOK A
UNITS 1–40

Oxford University Press

Oxford University Press
Walton Street, Oxford OX2 6DP

Oxford New York
Toronto Delhi Bombay Calcutta
Madras Karachi Petaling Jaya
Singapore Hong Kong Tokyo
Nairobi Dar es Salaam
Cape Town Melbourne Auckland

and associated companies in
Beirut Berlin Ibadan Nicosia

OXFORD is a trade mark of
Oxford University Press

ISBN 0 19 432237 8 (workbook A)
ISBN 0 19 432238 6 (workbook B)
ISBN 0 19 432241 6 (student's edition)
ISBN 0 19 432242 4 (teacher's edition)
ISBN 0 19 432243 2 (set of 3 cassettes)

First published 1982
Eighth impression 1987

Illustrations by:

Edward McLachlan

The publishers would like to thank the following for permission to reproduce copyright material:

The Bodley Head Ltd. for the extract from Graham Greene: 'Doctor Fischer of Geneva or The Bomb Party'; the Executors of the Ernest Hemingway Estate and Jonathan Cape Ltd. for the extract from David Garnett's introduction to Ernest Hemingway: 'The Torrents of Spring'; David Higham Associates Limited for the extract from Keith Waterhouse: 'Mondays, Thursdays' published by Michael Joseph; the Estate of the late Sonia Brownell Orwell and Martin Secker and Warburg Ltd. for the extract from George Orwell: 'Down and Out in Paris and London'; and The World Wildlife Fund for the use of their symbol.

Printed in Great Britain
at the University Printing House, Oxford
by David Stanford
Printer to the University

To the teacher

Workbook A of *Streamline English Destinations* consists of forty units. Each unit relates directly to the equivalent unit in *Streamline English Destinations* Units 1–40.

The *Workbook* is an optional element of the course, designed to provide language summaries and additional written exercises. It may be used in the following ways:

1 In more extensive courses as additional classroom material, providing extra oral practice and written reinforcement and consolidation of the basic core material in the student's edition.

2 As material for homework in more intensive situations.

The *Workbook* should only be used after full oral practice of the corresponding unit in the student's edition. The language summaries provide material for revision.

A further workbook is available for units 41–80 of the student's edition, under the title *Workbook B*.

Bernard Hartley
Peter Viney

Unit 1

Language summary

Greetings

Formal
A How do you do?
B How do you do?

Polite, friendly
A Hello. How are you?
B Very well, thanks, and you?
A I'm fine, thanks.

Very familiar, casual
A Hi!
B Hi!
A How's things?/How are you getting on?
B All right./O.K./Not bad.

Neutral
A Good morning/afternoon/evening.
B Good morning, etc.

Introductions

I'd like you to meet . . ./May I introduce . . .?/Hello, I'm . . .

Thanks and accepting thanks

A Thanks./Thank you./Thank you for coming to meet me.
B That's all right./Not at all.

Polite enquiries and responses

A How's work/the family?
B All right./O.K./Fine.
A Did you have a good trip?

Apologies

Sorry./I'm terribly sorry.
I'm afraid not.

Exercise

A ....
B ....
A ....
B ....

A ....
B ....

A ....
B ....
A ....
B ....

A ....
B ....
C ....

A ....
B ....
A ....
B ....

A ....
B ....
A ....
B ....

Look at the pictures. Read all the sentences carefully and use them in the spaces above to make conversations. Use each sentence once only.

A Oh, I'm terribly sorry!
A Annette! Hello, how are you?
B How do you do, Mr Grunt.
B Good morning, Mr Cobley.
A Hello, can I have your autograph?
B Yes, thanks. And thank you for coming to meet me.
B I'm afraid I'm not. Sorry.
A They're all O.K. Do you fancy a quick drink?
A Good morning, Mrs Cooper.
B Fine, how are you?
A Dad, this is Charley Grunt.
B Yes, I'd love one.
A Hello, Mike. I haven't seen you for ages.
B I beg your pardon?
B That's all right. It wasn't your fault.
A I'm all right. Did you have a pleasant flight?
B Good morning.
A Aren't you Paul McCartney?
C Hi!
B Hello, Peter. How's the family?
A May I introduce Tom Cobley? He's our new sales representative.

Unit 2

Language summary

I, He, She *It, We* *You, They*	*'ll* *will* *won't* *will not*	*be doing it*	*at 6.* *from 6 until 7.* *during the programme.* *for 10 minutes.*

The flight leaves at 8.30.
I'm meeting him tomorrow.
We'll begin at about 6.30.

Exercise 1 Timetables

A *When does the next flight to Rome leave?*
B *It leaves at quarter to nine.*
A *And at what time does it get to Rome?*
B *At five past eleven. It takes two hours and twenty minutes.*

Look at the timetables.
Make four more conversations like this.

	From	To	Depart	Arrive
FLIGHT	London	Rome	08.45	11.05
BUS	High Street	Crimea Road	10.00	10.20
TRAIN	Bristol	Swansea	17.15	18.53
BOAT	Dover	Calais	22.30	23.45
HOVERCRAFT	Calais	Ramsgate	14.30	15.10

Exercise 2

```
Keith Gordon is playing golf tonight.
He's meeting Tom Harris at 6 o'clock.
They'll drive to the golf course, and
they'll begin at about 6.30.
They'll probably finish at 9.00.
They'll be playing golf from 6.30 until 9 o'clock.
```

Use these words and write a similar paragraph:
Janet/tennis/Rosie/5.30/walk/tennis club/begin/5.45/finish 7.00

Exercise 3 Arrangements

Keith Gordon is the manager of an insurance company. This is his diary for tomorrow.

He's meeting Miss Granger at 9.15.

Make five more sentences.

5 Thursday 36.329

9-15 - Meet Miss Granger (new accounts clerk)
10-30 - Interview new secretary
11-00 - Visit High Street branch office
1-00 - Lunch, Mrs Stanton (Continental Computers)
3-00 - See Mr Palmer (Western Stationary)
6-00 - Golf Tom Harris

1 ....
....

2 ....
....

3 ....
....

4 ....
....

5 ....
....

Exercise 4

Vivian Townsend is a fashion buyer for a large department store. Tomorrow she's flying to Rome on business. This is her diary.

8.30 *What'll she be doing at 8.30?*
She'll be waiting for her flight at Heathrow Airport.

Write questions and answers for: 10.00/15.00/18.00/21.30/23.45.

14 Saturday 73·292
Sun rises 06.17 Sun sets 18.03 · Moon rises 11.31 Moon sets 02.53

FLIGHT BA 502 → ROME
(Depart Heathrow 0845, Arrive 1105)
N.B. Check in by 0820, Terminal I!
14.00-17.00 Signor Rossi, 'Mode' exports - new contract?
17.30 Visit Fashion show, British Trade Centre
21.00 Dinner, Signora Visconti
HOTEL TRAJAN, ROME (Check in by 23 00)

10.00 ....
....
....

15.00 ....
....
....

18.00 ....
....
....

21.30 ....
....
....

23.45 ....
....
....

Unit 3

Language summary

Name *What's your name? I'm/My name's (Jason Douglas).*

Date & Place of Birth *When/Where were you born? I was born on July 2nd/in London.*

Nationality *Where are you from?/Where do you come from? I'm British./I come from Britain.*

Marital Status *Are you married? Yes, I am./No, I'm not. I'm single.*

Address *What's your address?/Where do you live? I live at. . ./My address is (3280 Sunshine Boulevard).*

Education *Where were you educated?/Where did you go to (school)? I went to. . ./I was educated at Lane End Secondary School.*

Profession *What do you do?/What's your job? I'm an actor./I work in a bank.*

Exercise 1

Family Name	....	....	....
First Name(s)	....	....	....
Date of Birth	....	....	....
Place of Birth	....	....	....
Nationality	....	....	....
Address	....	....	....
	....	....	....
	....	....	....
Education	....	....	....
	....	....	....
Profession	....	....	....
Marital Status	....	....	....

Read these three texts and complete the forms above.

"*My name's Maria...Maria Montrose. Now, what can I tell you about myself? Let's begin at the beginning. I was born on March 23rd – I'd prefer not to tell you the year! I was the youngest of three children. I've got two brothers. Los Angeles is my home town. I was brought up and went to school there – Beverley Hills High, then on to Stanford University. I graduated in Drama. I got married in 1966 when I was only 23, but it broke up after a couple of years. Montrose was my ex-husband's name, but I still use it in my career. My maiden name was Mankowitz. I've been very lucky in my career as an actress. I still live in L.A. I've got an apartment in the San Andreas Tower on Sunset Drive.*"

"*I was christened Stanley after my father, Stanley George Hooper, who had been, among other things, the mayor of Preston. I've been a teacher all my life in different parts of the country. I now teach at Preston Grammar School, where I went to school myself before going on to Liverpool University to study English. I'm a widower now. My wife died three years ago and I live with my eldest daughter at 26, Poplar Avenue, Preston which is only a stone's throw from where I was born in 1925. I'm a great believer in astrology. I'm a Taurus myself, having been born on 25th May.*"

EDINBURGH EVENING NEWS 12 Dec

LOCAL GIRL OFF TO AFRICA

Jeannie Macpherson, who was in town visiting her parents for her birthday yesterday, is off to Kenya, where she'll be working in a national park. 22-year-old Jeannie was educated at the Carnegie Academy for Girls, and the University of St Andrews, where she has just qualified as a zoologist. Jeannie, of 17 Glencoe Road, is engaged to local dentist Hamish Maclean.

Exercise 2

1 Interview a student in your class and write a short biography of him/her like the one above.
2 Write a short autobiography.

Unit 4

Language summary

He's / *They've*	*been doing it*	*for 2 hours.* / *since 6 o'clock.*
	done (a lot).	

How	*long*	*have they* / *has he*	*been doing it?*
	much / *many*		*done?*

What will he be doing tomorrow?
He'll be doing (this).

How	*much* / *many*	*will*	*he* / *they*	*have done?*
He / *They*	*'ll* / *will*	*have done (a lot).*		

big/bigger/biggest *... as big as ...*
economical/more economical/the most economical

Exercise 1

How many cars were they making per week in February? 750.

Ask and answer for the other months on the graph.

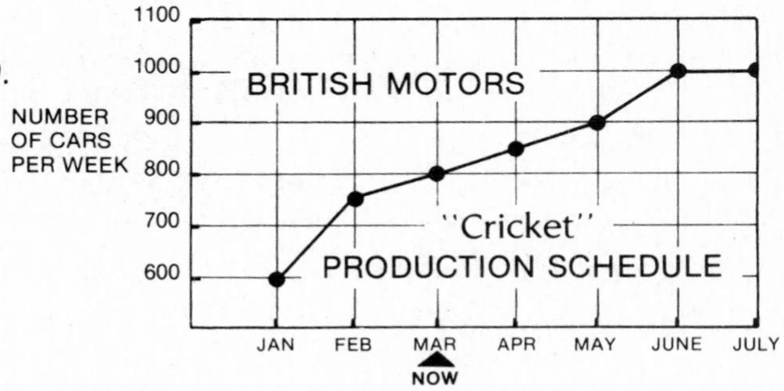

BRITISH MOTORS
"Cricket"
PRODUCTION SCHEDULE

NUMBER OF CARS PER WEEK: 1100, 1000, 900, 800, 700, 600

JAN FEB MAR APR MAY JUNE JULY

NOW

1 ...

2 ...

3 ...

4 ...

5 ...

6 ...

Exercise 2

Look at the graph.

They made 2,400 cars in January, 3,000 in February and 3,200 in March. So they have made 8,600 cars.

How many will they have made by the end of April?
They'll have made 11,600.

Ask and answer for May and June.

1 ...

2 ...

Exercise 3

David and Andrea Brent got married two years ago. They want to buy a house. They've both been working overtime, and they are able to save £100 a month. They began saving exactly one year ago, in July. They don't need to save all the money, but they need £2,500 as a 10% deposit. Write full answers.

How long have they been married? *They've been married for two years.*

1 How long have they been saving? ...

2 How much do they save monthly? ...

3 How much have they already saved? ...

4 How much will they have saved by December? ...

5 Will they have saved enough by next June? ...

6 When will they have saved enough? ...

Unit 5

Language summary

I	*enjoy* *love* *like* *don't like* *dislike* *can't stand* *hate*	*doing it.*	*I'm*	*afraid of* *terrified of* *frightened of* *scared of* *tired of* *bored with* *fed up with* *interested in*	*doing it.*	*I*	*began* *started* *stopped* *gave up*	*doing it.*

Exercise

Look at this.

football {
I like playing football.
My brother began playing football at school.
I enjoy reading about football.
She's fed up with watching football on T.V.
I'm always interested in hearing the football results.

or something else . . .

Now select one of the verbs from the language summary, and make a sentence using an '. . . ing' form with each of these words.

1 house ....

2 bed ....

3 job ....

4 friends ....

5 crowded airports ....

6 adventure stories ....

7 self-service restaurants ....

8 beach ....

9 classical music ....

10 money ....

11 spare time ....

12 on holiday ....

13 supermarket ....

14 cars ....

15 children ....

16 homework ....

17 English ....

18 advertisements on television ....

19 horror films ....

20 arguments ....

21 important people ....

22 quiz games ....

23 presents ....

24 alarm-clock ....

Unit 6

Look at this

Business Letters

Addressed to	Beginning	Ending
The Personnel Manager National Video Ltd. The Manager Western Insurance Co.	Dear Sir, Dear Madam, Dear Sir or Madam,	Yours, Yours faithfully, (GB) Yours truly, (GB or US)
J. Sainsbury plc The Midland Bus Company Messrs Welch and Cheater*	Dear Sirs, (GB) Gentlemen. (US) Dear Sir or Madam,	
Mr M. Smith/Michael Smith M. Smith, Esq., (GB formal)	Dear Mr Smith,	Yours sincerely, Yours,
Mrs Smith† Miss Smith Ms Smith	Dear Mrs Smith, Dear Miss Smith, Dear Ms Smith,	

Notes

* 'Messrs' is used for two or more persons, e.g. Messrs Brown and Green/Messrs Williams and Son/Messrs Arkwright Bros. (brothers). But is not used for limited companies, e.g. Alan and White Ltd/Macdonald and Sons plc (public limited company).

† When signing a letter, women often put 'Mrs' or 'Miss' in brackets after the name, e.g. Mary Green (Miss). If you are replying to a letter and you do not know if it is 'Mrs' or 'Miss', then you can write 'Mary Green' or 'Ms M. Green'.

Exercise 1

Imagine you are being interviewed by a careers officer. Complete the conversation.

Careers Officer Please take a seat.

You ....

Careers Officer Now, What's your name?

You ....

Careers Officer Ah, yes. Now, where did you go to school?

You ....

Careers Officer Fine. What about qualifications ... er ... exam passes?

You ....

Careers Officer What about school subjects ... which were your favourite ones?

You ....

Careers Officer And your best ones?

You ....

Careers Officer What subjects didn't you like studying?

You ....

Careers Officer Why?

You ....

Careers Officer And hobbies ... what do you like doing in your spare time?

You ....

Careers Officer What sort of job do you want to do?

You ....

Careers Officer Why do you think you'd like doing that?

You ....

Careers Officer Well, thank you very much.

continued

Exercise 2

Look at this.

CHILDREN'S NURSE required for British Family with two children (ages 2 and 5) living in Brussels. Driving licence essential. French an advantage. Please write giving brief details of qualifications and experience to: Mrs Arnold, International Employment Agency, 12, Knight Street, London W4A 2BZ

Here is a reply to the advertisement. Write it out with the correct layout and punctuation.

4 king henry avenue stratford england 30th july 1982 mrs arnold international employment agency 12 knight street london W4A 2BZ dear mrs arnold i saw the advertisement for a children's nurse in todays daily mail i am a qualified nanny with a national diploma in childrens nursing from the stratford institute for further education i have been working as a nanny in paris for the last year and i am very interested in this position i speak good french and hold a current driving licence i enclose a testimonial from my previous employer i look forward to hearing from you yours sincerely tricia potter miss

Exercise 3

Job advertisements may ask you for a 'c.v.' or 'curriculum vitae'. Look at the advertisement, the curriculum vitae and the letter of application.

SHORTHAND-TYPIST Opportunity for junior shorthand-typist with travel agency. Please send c.v. with application – Box No. 342, Charchester Evening Post, Hornby St, Charchester CHI 1WX.

Curriculum vitae

Name	Viola Hathaway
Address	Flat 2, Midsummer Court, Primrose Gardens, Charchester, CH8 3UB
Date of Birth	13/12/65
Education	Northam Comprehensive Appleby School of Commerce
Qualifications	CSE in English, Maths, Biology, French, Appleby School of Commerce Diploma in shorthand and typing
Experience	None
Interests	travel, dancing, music
Reference	Mrs Angela Appleby, B.A. Appleby School of Commerce, High Street, Charchester, CH2 4AY.

Flat 2, Midsummer Court,
Primrose Gardens,
Charchester CH8 3UB

4th September 19

Box No. 342
Charchester Evening Post

Dear Sirs,

I would like to apply for the position of shorthand-typist. I have just completed a one-year course in commercial studies at the Appleby School of Commerce. I enclose my curriculum vitae.

Yours faithfully,

Viola Hathaway

Viola Hathaway (Miss)

Look at these two advertisements. Reply to one of them. Write out your own curriculum vitae, a letter of application, and the envelope.

SALES PERSONS wanted for expanding department store, in record department, ladies fashions, electrical goods and bookshop. Please write with c.v. to Sparks and Fraser plc, Oxford St, London, WA7 36Y.

CLERK required for general office duties. Good opportunity for school leaver. Excellent prospects for promotion. Apply, enclosing c.v., to Cox and Rogers, Bourne Avenue, Tadworth, TTH2 8PV.

Unit 7

Language summary

Verb + infinitive

hope to (do)	*want to (do)*	*manage to (do)*	*threaten to (do)*
refuse to (do)	*would like to (do)*	*decide to (do)*	*had to (do)*
plan to (do)	*intend to (do)*	*demand to (do)*	*have to (do)*
offer to (do)	*expect to (do)*	*need to (do)*	*going to (do)*
agree to (do)	*promise to (do)*	*arrange to (do)*	

Exercise

Bank crisis
'NO COMMENT' was all the Chairman of Southland Bank would say this morning. The bank closed its doors at noon on Tuesday and has not opened since.

(refuse) *The Chairman refused to comment.*

Continue.

Another fighter crashes
ANOTHER F42 fighter plane has crashed. It happened over the English Channel this morning. The pilot escaped unhurt. He ejected two miles off the coast and was picked up by an air/sea rescue helicopter.

1 (manage) ....

....

Factory sit-in
FACTORY WORKERS at Darnley Chemicals are continuing their sit-in in protest at the management's closure proposals. A spokesman for the workers said 'We shall not be moved'.

2 (refuse) ....

....

Tax cuts on the way
THERE WILL be tax reductions in the next financial year. 'We will not break our word to the people who voted for us at the last election', the Prime Minister stated at a City banquet last night.

3 (promise) ....

....

Olympic gold?
BEN DOE, the British 400-metre champion, ran his fastest time this year at Crystal Palace last night. After the race Doe commented 'Now for the Olympics. Only the gold will be good enough for me'.

4 (expect) ....

....

Nurses offered 8%
AN INCREASE of 8% is the latest pay offer to nurses. The government say that this is their final offer, but nurses' leaders will probably press for further negotiations.

5 (offer) ....

....

Stan Walsh unhappy
EASTFIELD UNITED manager Brian Huff admitted today that he had received a transfer request from striker Stanley Walsh. Walsh has been unhappy at Eastfield for some time and feels that he would be happier with a new club.

6 (would like) ....

....

July summit
IT WAS announced today that world leaders will meet in London in July. There has been some disagreement about the time and place, but these problems have now been solved.

7 (agree) ....

....

New by-pass for Tadworth
TADWORTH Council voted 20–16 in favour of a new by-pass last night. The decision came after weeks of discussion. The work will begin next spring and should take eighteen months to complete.

8 (decide) ....

....

Strike threat
MINERS' LEADERS are very unhappy with the Coal Board's latest pay offer of £10 a week on basic pay. The miners will vote on Wednesday but miners' leaders have already said that they will recommend industrial action.

9 (threaten) ....

....

Spring wedding of the year
THE DUKE of Mercia yesterday announced his engagement to Lady Diana Marks, the second daughter of Earl Marks. The wedding will take place in April. The Duke, aged 42, met Lady Diana, 22, in St. Moritz last winter.

10 (intend) ....

....

Unit 8

Language summary

Adjective + infinitive

I	*'m* / *was*	*delighted to (hear) . . .* / *willing to (help) . . .*
He / *She*	*is* / *was*	*sorry to (lose) . . .* / *happy to (gain) . . .*
We / *You* / *They*	*are* / *were*	*sad to (learn) . . .* / *ready to (help) . . .* / *surprised to (hear) . . .* / *upset to (hear) . . .*

It	*is* / *was* / *will be* / *has been*	*lovely to (hear) . . .* / *nice to (know) . . .* / *difficult to (know) . . .* / *great to (be) . . .* / *interesting to (look at) . . .*

You don't look (old) enough to (be) . . .
I was too (ill) to (come) . . .

Informal letter endings

Love,
Lots of love,
All my love,
(Very) Best wishes,
All the best,
Yours sincerely,

Exercise 1

I heard about all your problems. I was very sad.
I was very sad to hear about your problems.

Continue.

1 I'll be able to help you next week. You know that I'm always willing.

....

2 You can send that cheque today. It's ready.

....

3 Congratulations! I read about the birth of your son in the paper. I was really delighted!

....

4 I was surprised when I saw you on T.V. last night.

....

5 We found out about the burglary at your home this morning. All of us were upset.

....

6 I'm sorry, but I must say that this work isn't good enough!

....

7 We received your photographs in today's post. We were very happy.

....

8 It was great! We were on holiday in Italy for two weeks.

....

9 It was interesting. We went round all the art galleries in Florence.

....

10 We visited St. Mark's Square in Venice. It was lovely.

....

11 It was nice. We had excellent food every day.

....

12 It will be difficult. We'll have to eat English food again when we get back from holiday!

....

Exercise 2

Look at this.

SAN JOSE. **Almería.** - Serie 92, n. º62
Playa de los Genoveses
Plage des "Genoveses"
"Genoveses" Beach
Strand der "Genoveses"

Dear Malcolm and Shirley,
Here we are in sunny Spain! It's great to have really hot weather every day. We're being very lazy, but sometimes it's just nice to lie on the beach doing nothing. Andy was surprised to find that people could understand his Spanish! It was difficult to go to all those evening classes last winter, but now he's delighted to be able to use it. That's all for now – back to the beach!

Very best wishes, love Sharon & Andy.

Mr. and Mrs. Temple,
83, Winston Avenue,
SOUTHAMPTON SO 17 9BG
England.

Kolor-Zerkowitz

Impresión: Casamaió ·Barcelona

John and Ellen Ross are on holiday in London. Use these prompts and write a card to their friends, Bobby and Pam Barnes in Dallas, Texas. They live at 1134, Westfork Boulevard.

interesting/museums and palaces/surprised/discover/hotel prices/very high/not difficult/get round London/great/the Queen/Buckingham Palace/happy/you again/next week/pleased/you willing/us/at the airport/nice/home

Exercise 3

Imagine that you are on holiday in a foreign country. Choose a place, and write a postcard to some friends at home.

Exercise 4

She's a university professor, but she looks pretty stupid!
She doesn't look intelligent enough to be a university professor.

Continue.

1 She's a doctor. She looks very young.

....

....

2 He's a professional footballer. He looks pretty old to me.

....

....

3 He's a famous boxer. He looks pretty weak!

....

....

4 That car won the Monte Carlo Rally. It looks pretty slow!

....

....

Unit 9

Language summary

Someone	*advised* *allowed* *encouraged* *expected* *forbade* *forced* *helped* *invited* *persuaded* *preferred* *reminded* *told* *wanted*	*me* *you* *him* *her* *us* *them* *Malcolm* *the children*	*to (do)*	*something.*
It	*embarrassed*			

I'm (not)	*here* *there*	*to*	*do it.* *listen.* *give an opinion.*

He's	*too*	*young* *tired*	*to (do) it.*

We seem to have rows all the time.

Exercise 1

'If I were you, Mrs Huggins, I'd take traveller's cheques,' said the Bank Manager.

(advise) *The Bank Manager advised her to take traveller's cheques.*

Continue.

1 'Don't forget to fasten your seat belts,' the flight attendant said.

(remind) ....

....

....

2 'I can't fill in this form,' he said. 'Don't worry, I'll help you,' said the secretary.

(help) ....

....

....

3 'Would you like to see my paintings, Judy?' he said.

(invite) ....

....

....

4 'Stay on at school, Sandra, and take your exams,' the careers officer said.

(advise) ....

....

....

5 'You must play well today,' the manager said, 'it's the most important match of the season.'

(want) ....

....

....

6 'Business should improve soon,' said the Minister.

(expect) ....

....

....

7 'Go away, all of you!' she shouted. 'Leave me alone!'

(tell) ....

....

....

8 'You can't come into this discotheque wearing jeans, Miss,' the doorman said.

(not allow) ....

....

....

9 'You mustn't come home late,' said Sarah's father.

(forbid) ....

....

....

10 'Can I go out, Dad?' 'Well, I think you really should stay in and finish your homework.'

(prefer) ....

....

....

11 'Don't be too disappointed, Mr Jones. Take the test again. You'll probably pass it next time,' the driving instructor said.

(encourage) ....

....

....

12 'Don't argue. Just follow that car!' the policeman ordered the taxi-driver. 'All right, all right . . .' he replied.

(force) ....

....

....

13 'I'd rather not do it.' 'Oh, come on, Sam, you must.' 'No . . . really.' 'Oh, come on.' 'Oh . . . all right then.'

(persuade) ....

....

....

14 'I didn't want to do it. It was too embarrassing . . . but I had to,' he said.

(embarrass) ....

....

....

Exercise 2

Read this statement. Complete the spaces, selecting verbs from the language summary. Do not use the same verb twice.

Tadworth Police

Statement by *Police Constable Dixon*

Date *27th February*

I was walking along Blenheim Street at approximately 12 o'clock when I saw the accused standing outside the Flamingo Club. They were arguing with the doorman. I made enquiries and the doorman said, "These young men are not members of the club, and I refused to .... them to come in. They said a friend had .... them to come to the club. I still .... them to enter and .... them to go away". I .... the three accused youths to go home. They said they didn't .... to go home, but I .... them to move along the street. However, when I returned ten minutes later one of the accused, Wayne Mason, was fighting with the doorman. Apparently they had tried to .... the doorman to let them in, and when he refused, the fight had started. The other youths were .... Mason to fight the doorman. The doorman .... me to arrest the youths.

P.C. Dixon.

Unit 10

Language summary

do and *make*.

He went somewhere to do something.
I'd made some arrangements.

Exercise 1

Complete the spaces with the appropriate forms of 'do' and 'make'.

STAN SLADE - PRIVATE EYE

My name's Slade, Stan Slade, private investigator. The story begins one Saturday morning in June . I hadn't been very busy. In fact I'd __________ only two jobs in a month. This big fat guy came into my office. He looked rich, very rich indeed – you know, fur coat, big cigar. He threw $1,000 on the table. He said, 'That's for one week. You're working for me.' Well, I don't usually __________ $1,000 in a month. 'What __________ you want me to __________ ?' I said. He sat down.
'This is an important job, Slade. I don't want you to __________ any mistakes, O.K.? I want you to __________ arrangements to follow my wife. Here's her photograph. She's much younger than me and -well, I want to know everything she __________ , everything! I want to know what time she gets up, when she __________ the housework when she __________ the beds, when she __________ the washing-up. I want every detail. Find out when she goes out, where she __________ the shopping and what she buys. I want to know when she __________ a phone call, and who she phones. Can you __________ that?' 'Sure,' I said. 'She won't know I'm there. I won't __________ any fuss, and I won't __________ any noise.'
'Right,' said the big guy. 'By the way, can I __________ a suggestion?' 'Sure, you're paying,' I said.
'__________ sure she doesn't see you. She's got some nasty friends, and they could __________ a lot of trouble for you.'
The fat guy left my office. I looked at the photo he'd given me, and the address. 'Well,' I thought to myself, 'I suppose I should go out and __________ some work'.

Exercise 2

9-00 Got up, made	Supermarket - groceries
coffee	Drugstore - shampoo,
10-45 Left house	vitamin pills
Service station - gas ($30)	Newstand - magazine
Coffee shop - made a	Dress shop - collect coat
phone call	11-32 return home

These are some of Slade's notes.
Service station – gas ($30)
She went to the service station to get some gas.
Write five more sentences like this.

Exercise 3

This is the rest of Slade's story. Complete the spaces with the appropriate forms of 'do' and 'make'.

It was pretty boring. I hoped that she would __________ something interesting, but nothing happened. On the third day I parked outside her apartment building, as usual. I began __________ a crossword. I heard footsteps. Suddenly there was a tap on the window. I looked up. It was my old buddy, Lieutenant O'Casey of the 18th Precinct, Los Angeles Police Department.
'__________ me a favour, O'Casey,' I said, 'go away. I've got a job to __________ .' 'So have I, Slade,' he replied. 'A lady has __________ a complaint. She says you've been following her. Have you been trying to __________ a date or something ?' 'O.K, O.K., O'Casey. I'm working for her husband.'
'Don't __________ me laugh, Slade! She isn't married. Who's paying you?' I described the fat guy . O'Casey laughed. '__________ he ask you to __________ a report on all her movements ?' 'That's right'.
'Well,' said O'Casey slowly, 'the lady is Laura Van Gilt, the millionairess. You remember, her father __________ a fortune out of soya beans. This fat guy sounds like Pete Greenstreet, the international jewel thief!'

Unit 11

Language summary

Requests and enquiries

Lend me 20p.
Shut the door, will you?
Do you want a coffee?
Would you like a coffee?

Can I *Could I* *May I* *Might I* *Do you mind if I* *I wonder if I could*	*ask you something?*
Would you mind if I	*asked you something?*

Would you mind doing something?
I wonder if you'd mind doing something?
Would you be kind enough to do it?
Would you be so kind as to do it?
I wonder if you can/could help me?

Not at all.
I don't mind at all.
Thank you so much.
No, thanks. I'm just looking.

Note. *When you make a polite request, it is often the way that you say something which is important, not the choice of a particular expression. You can say 'I wonder if you'd mind helping me?' in a rude way, or 'Give me 20p, please,' in a polite and friendly way.*

Exercise 1

You're in a hot and stuffy room. The corridors are closed.
Would you mind opening a window?

1 Your case is on a luggage rack. It's much too heavy for you to lift down.

....

....

2 You have just answered the phone. There's a pan of milk on the cooker, and it's boiling over.

....

....

3 You work in an office. You're talking to a very important customer. Another employee has just come in. (She didn't knock on the door). She wants you to sign a birthday card for the office boy.

....

....

4 You're in a shoe shop. The assistant has shown you several pairs of shoes, but you really want to see a pair in the window.

....

....

5 It's a cold winter's day.
Someone has just opened a window.

....

....

Exercise 2

You want to ask someone a very personal question. You can say:

A *May I ask you something?*
or **B** *Do you mind if I ask you something?*
or **C** *Would you mind if I asked you something?*

Write three questions for each of these.

1 You want to leave work early tonight. Ask your boss.

2 You're in someone's house. You feel like having a cigarette.

3 You've just discovered that you haven't got any money. The banks close in twenty minutes. Ask your boss for permission.

4 You're at a party. You've just been introduced to 'Nicola Barker'. She's about the same age as you. You don't want to address her as Miss Barker.

Exercise 3

1 You're in a shop. The assistant has just said 'Can I help you?' You only came into the shop because it's raining. What might you say?

2 You're sharing a table in a restaurant. The other person at the table has just said, 'Do you mind if I smoke?' You're a smoker yourself. What do you say?

3 You're in a queue in a self-service restaurant with your best friend. You haven't got any change. You need 35p for a cup of coffee. What do you say to him?

4 You're at a friend's house and you have to make an important long distance phone call. What do you say?

5 You go into a café. The only free seat is at a table with other people. What might you say to them?

6 You're on the beach, sunbathing. The people next to you have their radio on, and it's annoying you. What might you say?

Unit 12

Language summary

Noun + infinitive	Pronoun/adverb + infinitive	Verb + infinitive
I've got three more shirts to pack. *Have you got a book to read on the plane?* *Which key? The key to lock the case.*	*Is there anywhere to put it?* *There's nothing to worry about.* *You've got somewhere to stay tonight.*	*Remember to do . . ./forget to do . . .*

Exercise 1

Mr Stephens has just arrived at the Haughty Towers Hotel. His room isn't ready yet.

Mr Stephens *Is there anywhere to leave my bags?*
Receptionist Yes, you can leave them with the hotel porter, over there.

What other questions with '. . . anywhere to . . .' might he ask?

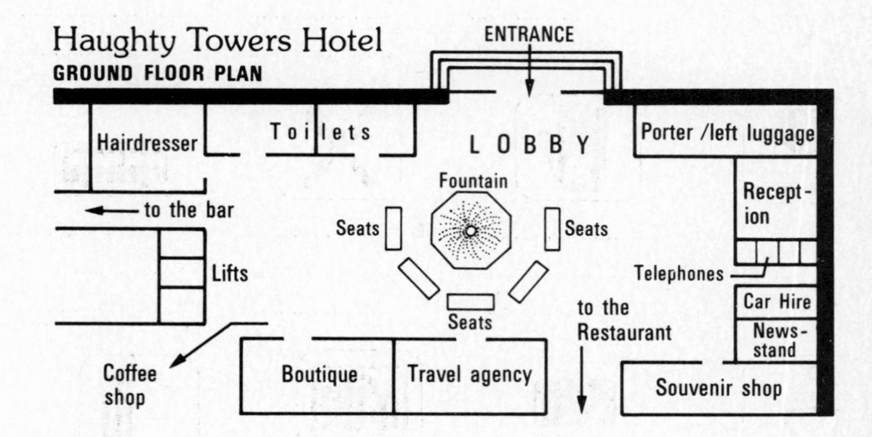

Exercise 2

Haven't you finished packing yet? (3 more shirts)
No, I've got three more shirts to pack.

1 Have you finished work yet? (several more letters)

....

....

2 Have you done all your homework? (2 more exercises)

....

....

3 Haven't you finished that book yet? (4 more chapters)

....

....

4 Have you addressed all the letters yet? (a few more)

....

....

5 Have you made all the arrangements? (a couple more phone calls)

....

....

Exercise 3

The Livingstone family are on their first camping holiday. They've just unloaded the car, and they've forgotten several important things.

1 *They remembered to bring some tins, but they forgot to bring a tin-opener.*

Look at the pictures below and write four more sentences.

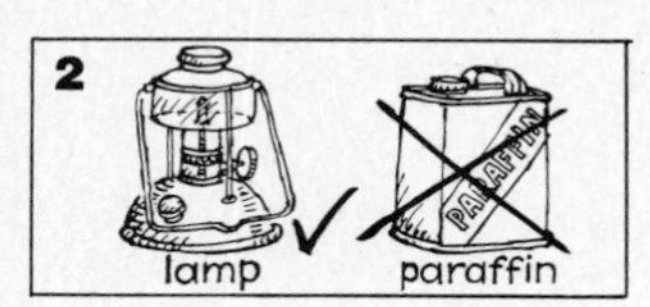

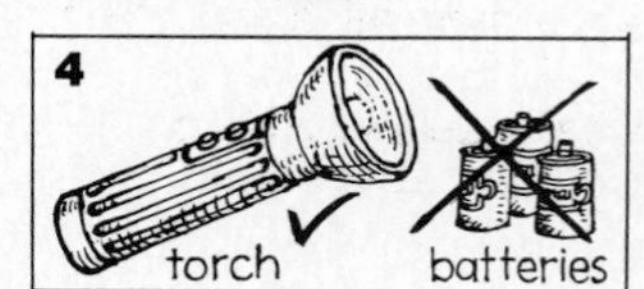

Exercise 4

Robin Caruso is a television presenter. For his latest documentary 'Survival', he's spending two weeks on a desert island with a cameraman. They haven't got any food.

They've just got these things: an axe/a gun/some fish-hooks/some matches/a hammer and nails/a two-way radio/a pen and paper/a magnifying glass/some books/plenty of fresh water/a knife.

They've got a two-way radio to use in emergencies.

Write ten more sentences.

Unit 13

Exercise 1

1 *Car Hire*

2 ....

3 ....

4 ....

5 ....

6 ....

7 ....

8 ....

9 ....

10 ....

11 ....

12 ....

13 ....

14 ....

15 ....

16 ....

17 ....

18 ....

These are some of the signs which you might see at an airport. Look at the example.
Look at the expressions below. Put the correct ones under the signs.

Information	Emergency Medical Services	Customs	Chapel
Bar	Hotel Reservations	Banks and Currency Exchange	Restaurant
Self-help trolleys	Airline Bus	Nursery	Disabled Facilities
Taxis	Passport Control	Post Office	Transfer Passengers
Baggage Reclaim			

Exercise 2

LONDON – LISBON

DEPART London, Heathrow Airport, Terminal 2 (Minimum check-in-time 60 mins)
London, Gatwick Airport [G] (Minimum check-in-time 20 mins)

ARRIVE Lisbon Airport

(a) – 707 on Th Fr Sa 25 Jun – 1 Aug
(b) – 707 on Su 28 Jun – 2 Aug
(y) – One hour earlier from 27 Sep

Frequency	Aircraft Dep	Aircraft Arr	Via	Transfer Times	Flight	Air-craft	Class & Catering
Daily	**1055** [G]	**1330(y)**	**non-stop**		**BA436**	**73S**	**CM** ◑
Daily ex We Su	1440	1705(y)	non-stop		TP453	727(a)	Y ⊗
We Su from 1 Apr	1440	1705(y)	non-stop		TP463	727	Y
Mo Th Su	**1640** [G]	**1915(y)**	**non-stop**		**BA438**	**73S**	**CM** ◑
Th Su from 9 Aug	1825	2205(y)	Oporto		TP485	727(b)	Y ⊗

Look at this conversation.

A Would you mind giving me some information about flights to Lisbon?
B Not at all. Which day of the week would you like to travel?
A Sunday, if possible.
B What time of day?
A As early as possible.
B Then I'd recommend the 10.55 flight – it gets in at 1.30.
A Does that go from Gatwick or Heathrow?
B Gatwick.
A Yes, that would be all right.

Now write a similar conversation for someone who wants to fly late on Thursday.

Exercise 3

Some British friends are coming to your country for a short stay.

Write down five things that you would recommend them to do. *I'd recommend them to hire a car.*

Exercise 4

Imagine that you are planning a visit to Britain.
What would you like to see?
What would you expect to eat?
What would you hope to do?

Unit 14

Language summary

It is / *They are*	*used for doing something.*

Filling station, cooking oil, boxing glove, waiting room, sleeping pill, etc.

Someone does it . . . it is done.
Someone should do it . . . it should be done.
Someone can do it . . . it can be done.

Someone cannot do it . . . it cannot be done.
Someone's doing it . . . it's being done.
Someone must do it . . . it must be done.

Exercise 1

Read this carefully. It is part of a leaflet issued by The National Westminster Bank.

Use the blank cheque below, and write out a cheque to the Wessex Gas Company for £98–05.

Know your cheques

Cheque counterfoil
This will help you keep an accurate record of your account.

Cheque number
This number identifies the particular cheque and should be quoted in correspondence concerning the cheque.

Crossing
These two parallel lines indicate that the cheque is 'crossed'. This safeguards both you and the recipient as the cheque can only be paid into a bank account and cannot be cashed.

Your account number
This number is unique to your account and will need to be quoted when crediting your account with cash or cheques.

The account name
This is the way your branch will know your account, and should be quoted together with the account number in any correspondence.

Bank sorting code
This combination of numerals identifies your branch when the cheque is being processed by the Bank.

Writing your cheques

Cheque counterfoil
Enter the date, the amount paid and the payee when you write the cheque. This will enable you to keep an up-to-date record of your account.

Payee
Write the name of the individual or company to whom you are making payment here. Make sure it is in the complete form they require.

When withdrawing cash from the Bank write the word 'Cash' at this point.

Amount in words
Enter the amount in words at this point on the cheque. Ensure that no gaps are left in the cheque for fraudulent additions. The various acceptable alternative versions are shown below.

Date
Make sure you date your cheque clearly and include the day, month and year.

Signature
Be sure this is your normal signature, and that it matches the sample signature you gave to the Bank when opening the account. (Any alterations you make to the cheque when making it out must be initialled).

Amount in figures
Enter the amount in figures at this point on the cheque. Make sure it is the same as the amount in words. The various acceptable alternative versions are shown below.

Twenty-nine pounds 69	*£29·69*
Twenty-nine pounds 08	*£29·08*
Twenty-nine pence	*£0·29*

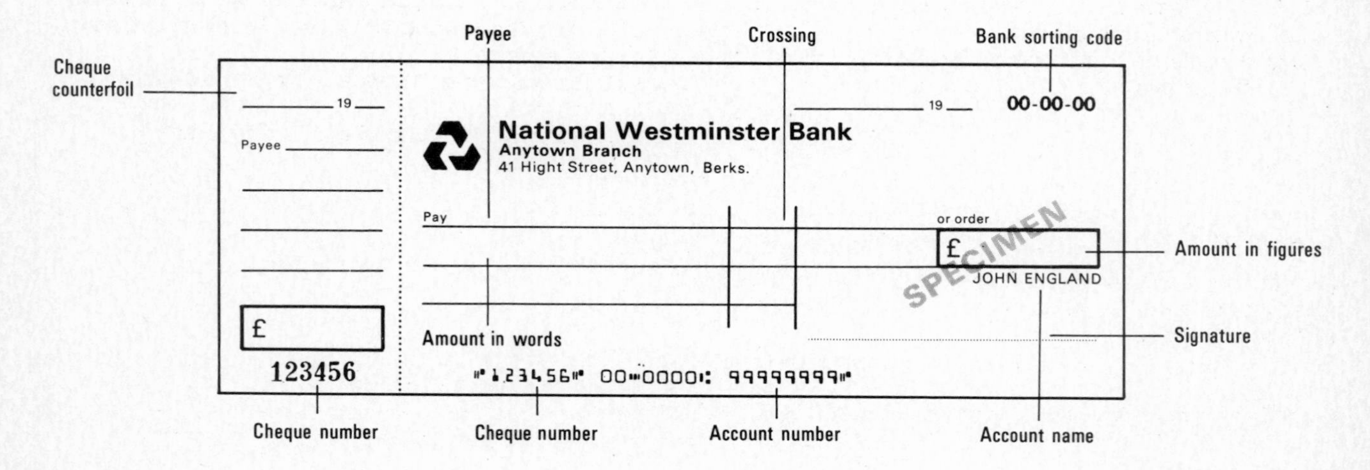

Exercise 2

Find words in the texts which mean:

1 a person who receives something.
2 something extra
3 the local office of a large organization.
4 a change.
5 section of a cheque kept by the sender as a record.
6 unfilled space.
7 exchange of letters.
8 person's name written by him/herself.
9 being the only one of its type.
10 person to whom something is paid.

Exercise 3

You should quote the number in any correspondence.
The number should be quoted in any correspondence.

Continue.

1 You can only pay the cheque into a bank account. ....

....

....

2 You cannot cash it. ....

....

3 You will need to quote the number. ....

....

4 The bank is processing the cheque. ....

....

5 Do not leave any gaps in the cheque. ....

....

6 We show the various acceptable versions below. ....

....

....

7 You must initial any alterations. ....

....

Exercise 4

This number identifies the cheque. *The cheque is identified by this number.*

Continue.

1 The bank sorting code identifies your branch.
2 You should write the name of the payee here.
3 You should write the word 'cash' here.
4 You must date your cheque clearly.
5 You should enter the amount in figures at this point.

Exercise 5

What do you think these sentences mean?

1 'Crossed cheques safeguard both you and the recipient.'
☐ **A** Crossed cheques are cheaper for both you and the recipient.
☐ **B** Crossed cheques are quicker for both you and the recipient.
☐ **C** Crossed cheques protect both you and the recipient.

2 'Ensure that no gaps are left for fraudulent additions.'
☐ **A** If you leave a gap, someone may dishonestly write in extra words or figures.
☐ **B** If you leave a gap, the bank may make mistakes when adding it up.
☐ **C** If you leave a gap, someone may think you want to cheat them.

3 'Be sure your normal signature matches the sample signature you gave to the bank.'
☐ **A** When you sign a cheque, always write your signature in the same place.
☐ **B** When you sign a cheque, be sure that your signature is the same as the one you gave to the bank.
☐ **C** When you sign a cheque, be sure that you use the same colour ink as in the signature you gave to the bank.

4 'Any alterations you make to the cheque must be initialled.'
☐ **A** John Smith would write 'John Smith' next to any alterations.
☐ **B** John Smith would write 'J. Smith' next to any alterations.
☐ **C** John Smith would write 'J.S.' next to any alterations.

Exercise 6

Look at the cheque on the previous page. Mr England wants to pay in some money to his bank. He has got a cheque for £85–00, another for £20, and £50 in £10 notes. See if you can complete the 'Bank Giro Credit'.

Date________________
Cashier's stamp and initials
A/c.________________
Cash________________
Cheques POs etc.________________
£

Date________________
Cashier's stamp and initials

bank giro credit

Destination Branch Code number
Bank
Branch where account is held
Account (Block Letters) & A/C No
Fee
NWB1450 Rev Nov 79-1
Paid in by
Details for advice to recipient
NAR

£20 notes	
£10 notes	
£5 notes	
£1 notes	
50p coin	
Other silver	
Bronze	
Total cash £	
Cheques, POs etc. (see over)	
No of Cheqs, P Os	£

Unit 15

I remember once booking into a Los Angeles hotel where I was handed a form asking me how I proposed to settle my bill. Since I proposed to settle in cash, I wrote 'Cash', and the desk clerk turned white under his California tan. You would have thought I was offering to pay him in Indian beads.

'You don't wish to utilise an accreditisation facility, Mr Waterhouse?' he said in that appalling jargon which I'm sure is now taught in high schools instead of English.

No thank you. I'll pay cash.

'Travellers' cheques, would that be, Mr Waterhouse?'

No. Cash. These things, Dollars.

I showed him a few greenbacks and he stared at them as if they were an interesting collection of foreign stamps.

'One moment, sir.'

He darted into the inner office and I saw secretarial heads craning over the partition and giving me the kind of look I expect they normally reserved for people trying to book in as Mr and Mrs Smith. In a moment the manager appeared.

'Glad to know you, Mr Waterhouse. We hope you'll have a pleasant stay with us, and for your further enjoyment at this time we'd like to extend accreditisation facilities. We accept any regular credit card or if it's your pleasure we'd be happy to bill your company.'

'I don't want accreditisation facilities, thank you. I want to pay cash.'

Again I produced my wad of dollars pointing out that on each one of them was printed in legible type:'This note is legal tender for all debts, public and private.'

The manager read the words for himself, checked the signature that had been put to this reckless promise (Dorothy Andrew Katia, Treasurer to the United States), and seemed to waver.

'As a formality, Mr Waterhouse, could I request that you produce some identification at this time?'

I showed him my passport, my driving licence, a bill for the water rates and a letter from my brother. He examined them with care.

'These seem to be in order, Mr Waterhouse. To facilitate our accounting process at this time, could I request that you pay in advance?'

So I coughed up my wretched hoard of dollars and he held them up to the light then put them away in a cupboard. One day, I imagine, he'll take them out and show them to his grandchildren.

I stayed in the hotel a week and every time I entered the foyer a man sitting near the water-cooler lowered his newspaper and gave me a funny look. I learned later that he was the hotel detective. He must have been told to keep an eye on the Limey bum who couldn't afford to live on credit.

From 'Taking the Credit', an article by Keith Waterhouse, in *Mondays, Thursdays.* Michael Joseph, 1976.

Exercise 1

Find words which mean:

1 lobby
2 readable
3 wild and foolish
4 ask
5 brown colour of sunburnt skin
6 a collection of banknotes folded or rolled together
7 language full of specialist words
8 hesitate
9 to move quickly and suddenly
10 banknotes in US dollars
11 a small ball of wood or glass with a hole through it
12 to make easy
13 to stretch one's neck to see something
14 a thin dividing wall
15 in normal use
16 go in

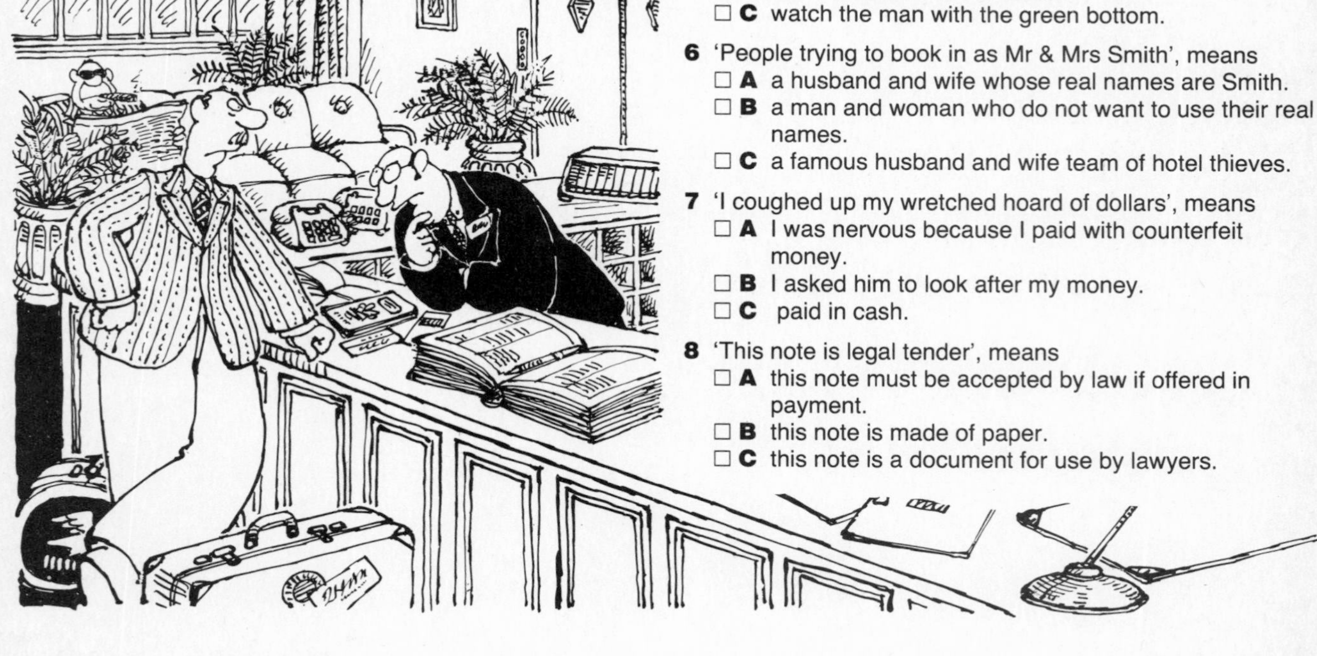

Exercise 2

1 'He turned white', because
☐ **A** he was embarrassed.
☐ **B** he was angry.
☐ **C** he was shocked.

2 'He gave me a funny look', means
☐ **A** he smiled at me.
☐ **B** he looked at me suspiciously.
☐ **C** he looked at me and laughed.

3 'We'd be happy to bill your company', means
☐ **A** we don't mind sending the account to your firm.
☐ **B** we'd like your company to send us a bill.
☐ **C** would you like us to telephone your company.

4 'To utilise an accreditisation facility', means
☐ **A** to borrow some money.
☐ **B** to pay by cheque.
☐ **C** to use a credit card.

5 'Keep an eye on the Limey Bum', means
☐ **A** watch the poor Englishman.
☐ **B** follow the cement salesman.
☐ **C** watch the man with the green bottom.

6 'People trying to book in as Mr & Mrs Smith', means
☐ **A** a husband and wife whose real names are Smith.
☐ **B** a man and woman who do not want to use their real names.
☐ **C** a famous husband and wife team of hotel thieves.

7 'I coughed up my wretched hoard of dollars', means
☐ **A** I was nervous because I paid with counterfeit money.
☐ **B** I asked him to look after my money.
☐ **C** paid in cash.

8 'This note is legal tender', means
☐ **A** this note must be accepted by law if offered in payment.
☐ **B** this note is made of paper.
☐ **C** this note is a document for use by lawyers.

Unit 16

Language summary

make/let	*someone*	*do*	*something.*
force/allow	*someone*	*to do*	*something.*

He was seen. He was driving a Land Rover.
He was seen driving a Land Rover.

I promised not to (do it).

Exercise 1

Norman Barker is in prison. He's writing to his mother. The letter begins:

Write five sentences with 'make', five with 'let' and five with 'don't let'.

Parkwood Maximum Security Prison

REGULATIONS, 'C' WING

All prisoners must

1 get up at 5 o'clock
2 go to bed at 7.30
3 clean their own cells
4 wear prison uniform at all times
5 work in the prison workshops
6 obey all orders from the warders

Prisoners may

1 have two visitors per month
2 write up to 3 letters a week
3 purchase cigarettes and sweets from the prison shop
4 earn up to £2 a week in the workshops
5 watch T.V. for 1 hour per day

Prisoners may not

1 have any alcoholic beverages
2 smoke in their cells
3 have radios or cassette-players
4 bring money into the prison
5 leave their cells without permission

SIGNED Harold McVicar, Prison Governor

Exercise 2

Joey Godber was in prison for two months. He has just been released. He says he was innocent, and is very angry about his time in prison. He's telling a friend about it.

'It was terrible! They forced us to get up at 5 o'clock. They only allowed us two visitors a month, and they didn't allow us to smoke in our cells!'

Write four sentences with 'forced', four with 'allowed' and four with 'not allowed'.

Exercise 3

Somebody saw him. He was driving a Land Rover.
He was seen driving a Land Rover.

Continue.

1 Somebody heard him. He was shouting for help. ....

....

....

2 Someone filmed her. She was waving to the crowds. ......

....

....

3 Somebody saw it. It was moving slowly. ....

....

....

4 Somebody recorded them. They were telling jokes. ....

....

....

5 Someone photographed them. They were swimming in the sea. ....

....

....

Unit 17

Language summary

I like it . . . I'd like to do it.
Which do you like best?

I prefer it . . . I'd prefer to do it.
Which do you prefer? Which would you prefer to do?

I'd rather do it./I'd rather not do it./I'd much rather do it.
Which would you rather do?

I like both.

I don't	*like*	*either*	*of them.*
	fancy	*any*	

There isn't much choice.
I can't make up my mind.

Entertainments

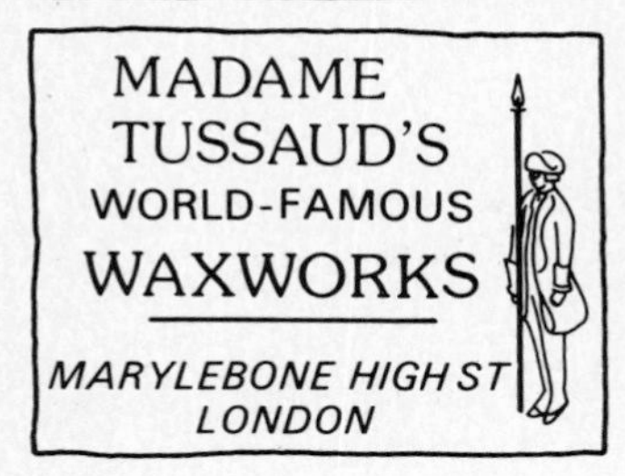

Exercise 1

waxworks/circus
Which would you prefer to see, the waxworks or the circus?
I'd prefer to see the waxworks.

Write questions and answers.

1 funfair/concert.
2 flying display/painting exhibition.

Exercise 2

speedway/wrestling
Where would you rather go?
I'd rather go to the speedway.

Write questions and answers.

1 football/tennis.
2 dance theatre/greyhound racing.

Exercise 3

Look at 'Entertainments'.

I'd like to see the speedway.
I wouldn't like to see the wrestling.

Write ten more sentences.

Exercise 4

How about wrestling or speedway tonight?
I'd rather go to the speedway.
or *I'd prefer to go to the speedway.*
or *I'd rather not see either.*
or *I don't fancy either. I'd much rather see the football.*

Now answer these questions.

1 Shall we go to the flying display or the dance theatre?
2 How about the circus or the concert?
3 Which do you fancy, the tennis or the greyhound racing?
4 Where would you rather go, the funfair or the waxworks?
5 I don't really fancy the football. I'd prefer to go to the painting exhibition. What about you?

Exercise 5

Look at the Language summary.
Answer these questions.

1 Which colour do you like best?
2 Which do you prefer, tea or coffee?
3 Where would you prefer to live, the city or the country?
4 Which would you rather eat, lamb or beef?

Unit 18

Language summary

They ought to (do it). They ought not to (do it). What ought they to do?

We	*'d*	*better*	*do it.*
	had	*better not.*	

Hadn't we better do it?

To spend time (doing something).
We've got a lot to do.
Winning has become the most important thing.

Exercise 1

I need some money, and the bank closes in 10 minutes.
You'd better go now. or *You'd better hurry.*

Continue.

1 We've got a long journey, and the petrol tank is almost empty.

....

2 He's getting married on Saturday, but he hasn't got a suit.

....

3 Her car's in a 'no parking' area and a policeman's coming.

....

4 He's just spilt coffee on her new dress.

....

5 It's her parents' wedding anniversary tomorrow.

....

6 There's a fire in the kitchen, and they can't put it out.

....

Exercise 2

Look at these signs. Make sentences about each one.

1 *You'd better not smoke.*

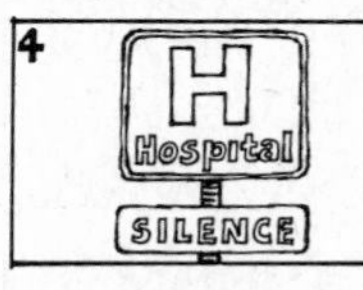

Exercise 3

Every day, I spend eight hours	*in bed.*
	sleeping.

I spend two hours watching television.

Make four sentences like this about yourself.

Exercise 4

It's important to win. *Winning is important.*

Make sentences.

1 It is dangerous to smoke.
2 It's easy to learn English.
3 It's a waste of time to get angry.
4 It's stupid to drive too fast.
5 It's relaxing to watch television.
6 It's nice to be on holiday.

Exercise 5

There is a local government election in Tadworth next week. The candidates for the North Tadworth district are Mike Legg and Marjorie Tyler. These are their election manifestos.

1 spend more money on education
2 stop building new roads
3 make the town centre into a pedestrian area
4 build more houses
5 introduce free buses for old people
6 increase local taxes

1 spend more money on the police
2 build a new motorway
3 don't make a pedestrian area (shopkeepers don't like the plan)
4 spend less on social services
5 build an airport near the town
6 don't increase local taxes

Mike Legg is speaking at a political meeting.
'I think they ought to spend more money on education. They're spending far too much on roads that we do not need. We ought not to build new roads.'

Make four sentences with 'ought(not) to' for Mike.

Make six sentences for Marjorie.

Unit 19

Exercise

Look at these sentences. Put the verbs in brackets in the correct form, 'do', 'to do' or 'doing'.

He enjoys *sitting* in the sun. (sit)

1 Put that cigarette out! You are not allowed .... in here. (smoke)
2 It's hot in here. Would you mind .... the window? (open)
3 He found the work difficult, but he managed .... the examination. (pass)
4 I never read Shakespeare now, because they made me .... it at school. (study)
5 She always travels by train or boat because she's afraid of .... (fly)
6 'Let's go out tonight.' 'All right. Where do you want ....?' (go)
7 You're overweight. You ought .... more exercise. (take)
8 This is a very beautiful village, but there's nowhere .... in the evening. (go)
9 When I first visited Britain, I couldn't get used to .... on the left. (drive)
10 There's a lot of traffic. We'd better not .... the road here. (cross)
11 I don't know why she resigned. She seemed .... very happy here. (be)
12 I'm tired of .... television every evening. (watch)
13 Her doctor advised her .... a specialist. (see)
14 I'll help you, I'm sure you aren't strong enough .... it on your own. (lift)
15 He spends all his time .... comics. (read)
16 My parents were very strict. They wouldn't let me .... out late in the evenings. (stay)
17 A kettle is used for .... water. (boil)
18 He's working too hard. He's too tired .... anything when he gets home. (do)
19 The robbers forced the manager .... the safe. (open)
20 I hope .... my brother in Australia next year. (visit)
21 He's not interested in .... money, his father's a millionaire. (earn)
22 Don't give up yet, we must keep .... (try)
23 I'd rather .... happy than rich. (be)
24 He needed bodyguards because several people had threatened .... him. (kill)
25 I was very happy .... your news. (hear)
26 Take your time. I don't mind .... (wait)
27 I'd rather not .... about that. (talk)
28 We're going to Oxford tomorrow. Would you like .... with us? (come)
29 He won't be long. He's just got two more phone calls .... (make)
30 She didn't want to go to work, so she pretended .... ill. (be)
31 I gave up .... five years ago. (smoke)
32 I'm bored with .... the same clothes every day. (wear)
33 The book was very difficult .... (understand)
34 Neither of them could find a job, so they both decided .... (emigrate)
35 She's very confident. She expects .... the election. (win)
36 I'm not here .... my time! (waste)
37 They won't let you .... the United States without a visa. (enter)
38 He joined the navy .... the world. (see)
39 I wonder if you'd be kind enough .... me? (help)
40 Charlie Chaplin films always make me .... (laugh)

Unit 20

Language summary

I'm certain . . . *I'm almost certain . . .*	*It must be . . .*
(I think) it's possible . . .	*It could be . . .* *It may be . . .*

(I think) it's possible, but unlikely . . .	*It might be . . .*
(I think) it's nearly impossible . . . *(I think) it's impossible . . .*	*It can't be . . .*

I thought it might be . . . (past)
I think it may be . . . (present)

Exercise 1

What's that in the sky? Is it from outer space?
(impossible) *It can't be from outer space.*

Continue.

1 Is this table Victorian?

(possible) ....

....

2 Who's that? I think it's Prince Charles!

(possible, but unlikely) ....

....

3 He's got a private plane. Is he very rich?

(almost certain) ....

....

4 That woman says she's 130 years old.

(almost impossible) ....

....

Exercise 2

A spy has 'bugged' this hotel room. (He's hidden a small microphone somewhere.) Where do you think it is?

It could be under the bed.
It might even be under the pillow.

Write sentences with 'could', 'may' and 'might'.

1 ....

2 ....

3 ....

4 ....

5 ....

6 ....

7 ....

8 ....

Exercise 3

'Mr J. Smith'
What do you think his first name might be?
It could be John. It could be James. It could be Joseph. It might be Julius!

Continue.

1 Miss M. Brown ....

2 Mr R. Green ....

3 Mrs J. Roberts ....

4 Mr B. Evans ....

5 Mr S. Williams ....

continued

Exercise 4

The police are looking for a murderer. They know it was a thin man of average height, in his 30s with short hair, a moustache and glasses. These are the six suspects in a police identity parade.

It can't be Chapman, because he hasn't got a moustache.

Write four sentences with 'can't', and one with 'must'.

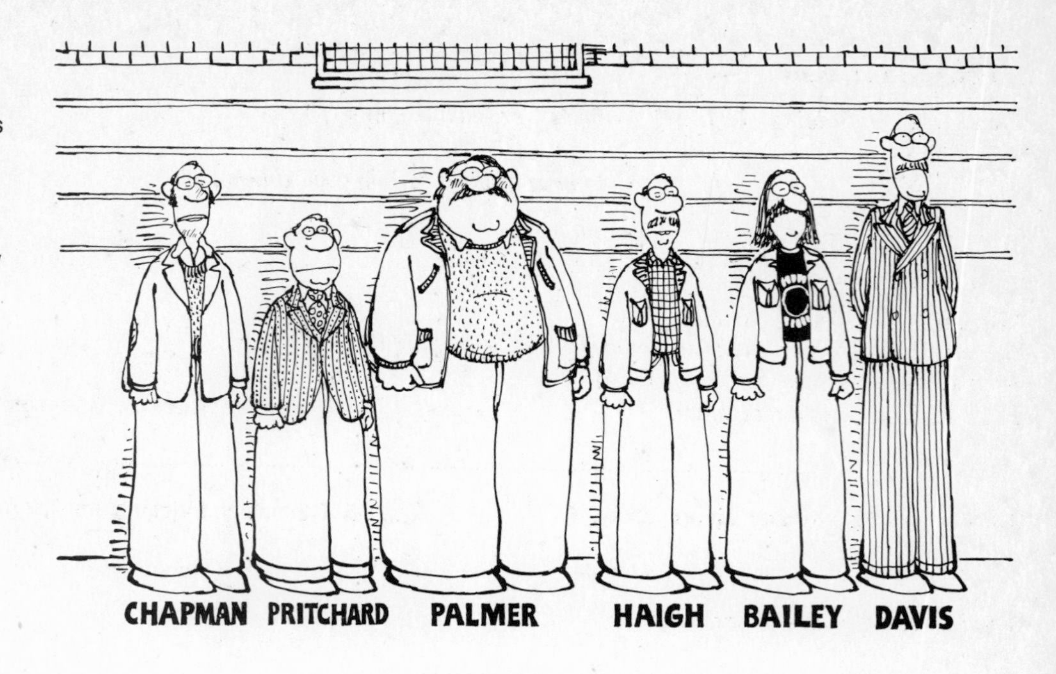

1 ....

2 ....

3 ....

4 ....

5 ....

Exercise 5

My grandmother can remember the first car in our town. *She must be very old.*
Continue.

1 My sister won the 'Miss World' beauty contest last year. ....

2 My father has got a Rolls-Royce and a Ferrari. ....

3 My brother's only twelve, but he's going to university next year. ....

4 My uncle's in prison. ....

5 My mother goes to church twice a day. ....

6 My cousin jumped off the Empire State Building. ....

7 My grandfather thinks he's Napoleon. ....

8 My aunt's a professional wrestler. ....

9 Our dog bites every visitor to the home. ....

10 My father-in-law hasn't washed for five years. ....

11 My nephew weighs 100 kilos. ....

12 My nieces are both champion gymnasts. ....

13 Our house has got five bedrooms. ....

14 My paintings have been exhibited in a gallery. ....

15 Three cars have crashed on that bend this year. ....

16 My brother-in-law runs for 10 km every morning. ....

Unit 21

Language summary

They	must may might can't	be doing (it).

She's	probably possibly	doing (it).

to have a row/a party/a good time/a look

Exercise 1

Catherine's sitting in the cinema.
She must be watching a film/She's probably watching a film.
What do you think these people are doing?

1 James is sitting in a restaurant.

....

2 Sarah's walking through an art gallery.

....

3 Richard's sitting in a football stadium.

....

4 Emma's in her car, on the motorway.

....

5 Thomas and Victoria are sitting in the library.

....

Exercise 2

California
Mexico City
Venezuela Bolivia Chile
Greenland
Most of Europe Zaíre
Moscow Iraq
Pakistan
Malaysia
Japan
New Zealand

International Date Line | AM | NOON | PM | AM

1.00 2.00 3.00 4.00 5.00 6.00 7.00 8.00 9.00 10.00 11.00 12.00 1300 1400 1500 1600 1700 1800 1900 2000 2100 2200 2300 2400

Alaska
Rocky Mountains
New York Montreal Colombia Peru
Eastern Brazil Argentina
Britain Algeria
Greece Turkey Egypt
Arabian Gulf Iran
India
China
Eastern Australia

Alaska's four hours behind Mexico. *China's eight hours ahead of Britain.*

Write four more sentences.

1 ....

....

2 ....

....

3 ....

....

4 ....

....

Exercise 3

Write four sentences using '... behind my country' and 'ahead of my country.'

1 ....

....

2 ....

....

3 ....

....

4 ....

....

continued

Exercise 4

What time is it in this country now? ....

Look at this example.

I live in Britain. I'm writing this at 2 p.m.
What do you think someone is doing in Alaska?
It's 3 a.m. *They must be sleeping/They're probably sleeping.*

What do you think someone is doing in Malaysia?
It's 9 p.m. *They're probably not working./They may be having dinner./They might be talking to some friends./They might be watching television.*

Choose six places, and write sentences about what people might be doing now.

Alaska. They must be sleeping. They're probably sleeping.

1 ....

2 ....

3 ....

4 ....

5 ....

6 ....

Exercise 5

Look! He's sawing that woman in half!
He can't be sawing her in half. It must be a trick.

Continue.

1 Look! He's eating fire! ....

....

....

2 Look! He's floating in mid-air! ....

....

....

3 Look! He's making that woman disappear! ....

....

....

4 Look! That dog's speaking to him! ....

....

....

5 Look! He's taking money from his ear! ....

....

....

6 Look! He's pulling rabbits from his hat! ....

....

....

7 Look! He's taking birds out of his mouth! ....

....

....

8 Look! He's swallowing a sword! ....

....

....

Unit 22

Language summary

They	should (not)/ought (not) to/are (not) supposed to had better (not)/would rather (not)	be doing it.

Exercise 1

Mr Tucker is a businessman. He's very overweight, and his company has just sent him to a health farm. It's his first day.

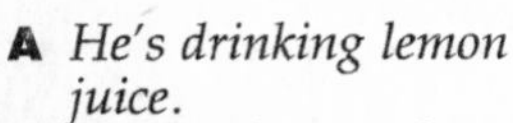

A *He's drinking lemon juice.*
B *He'd rather not be drinking lemon juice.*
C *He'd rather be drinking champagne.*

A ....

....

B ....

....

C ....

....

A ....

....

B ....

....

C ....

....

A ....

....

B ....

....

C ....

....

Exercise 2

CONINGHAM HALL HEALTH FARM

PATIENT	Robin Tucker
SCHEDULE	3rd December
6:30 - 7.00	Breakfast (1 glass lemon juice)
7.00 - 8.00	Running (5 km.)
8.00 - 8.15	Cold shower
8.30 - 9.15	Weight training, gym
9.30 - 9.50	Rowing machine
10.00 - 10.30	Sauna
10.30 - 11.15	Massage
11.30 - 12.00	Lunch (one carrot, one glass lemon juice)
12-30 - 13.00	Solarium
13.30 - 14.00	Swimming pool
14.15 - 15.15	Resting

It's the second day. Mr Tucker has disappeared from the health farm. They haven't been able to find him all morning.

At 6.45 the Director said: *'Where's Mr Tucker? He's supposed to be having breakfast!'*

What did he say at the following times?

7.30 ....

....

8.10 ....

....

8.45 ....

....

9.40 ....

....

10.15 ....

....

11.00 ....

....

11.45 ....

....

12.45 ....

....

1.45 ....

....

2.45 ....

....

continued

Exercise 3

Look at Exercise 2. Make sentences with 'He should be doing . . ' and 'He ought to be doing . . . .'

1 ....

2 ....

3 ....

4 ....

5 ....

6 ....

7 ....

8 ....

9 ....

10 ....

Exercise 4

At 3 o'clock the Director received a phone call from a nearby club. They asked him to come and collect Mr Tucker. When he got there, this is what he found.

Director *Mr Tucker! You aren't supposed to be sitting in a club!*

Write three more sentences.

1 ....

....

....

2 ....

....

....

3 ....

....

....

Exercise 5

Look at Exercise 4.
Make four sentences with 'You ought not to be doing . . .' and four with 'You shouldn't be doing . . .'

Exercise 6

The Director said, 'This isn't good enough, Mr Tucker. Coningham Hall is very expensive. If you want to stay, you'll have to follow our programme. If not, you'll have to leave and we will not be able to refund your money, so tomorrow, at 6.45 you'd better be having breakfast!'

Look at the Schedule in Exercise 2, and write ten sentences with 'You'd better . . .' and four sentences with 'You'd better not . . .'

Unit 23

THE GIANT PANDA

The giant panda is probably the most valuable and popular zoo animal. They live in the steep mountains of Western China. About 1000 giant pandas still survive in the wild, but only a very few have ever been seen alive outside China. In 1961 it was adopted as the symbol of the World Wildlife Fund and the panda has become a familiar sight on T - shirts, badges and carstickers. It is certainly popular with children and regularly rates in the top ten of children's favourite animals. The arrival of a panda at a zoo can turn a loss into a healthy profit.

Giant pandas can live for up to 20 years, and a big male can weigh 150 kilos. They live on a diet of rock-hard bamboo stems. They can eat 4 kilos at a sitting and may chew for 12 hours a day. Their dependence on bamboo is the main threat to their survival. The bamboo plant dies off about every 100 years and when this last happened in 1975, nearly 150 pandas died. This threat of extinction has led to the setting up of a panda research centre in China with $1 million being contributed by the World Wildlife Fund.

More than 30 giant pandas have been born alive in Chinese zoos. The first breeding in captivity was at Peking zoo in September 1963. The mother, Li-Li, cradled her infant, Ming-Ming, in her arms day and night. The first two births in the West were both to Ying-Ying in Mexico City zoo. Unfortunately she rolled over on the first baby and crushed it. The second was born in 1981. It is not easy to mate pandas in captivity and in the late '60's Chi-Chi, from London zoo, and An-An, from Moscow zoo, had a very on-off romance with no results.

A new born panda weighs only 125 grams and measures less than 15 cm. The female panda is 800 times heavier than her baby at birth and the baby is 3 – 4 months old before it can crawl. It is pinkish-white at birth without dark markings and the familiar black eyes.

Although very slow moving and peaceful, the panda can be vicious when angry. A keeper at Chicago zoo was so badly mauled by Mei-Lai, a big male panda, that he had to have his arm amputated. But for most of us the giant panda remains a lovable, cuddly, living teddy bear.

Exercise 1

1 'Their dependence on bamboo is the main threat to their survival', means
- ☐ **A** they often fall from bamboo plants and injure themselves.
- ☐ **B** the unreliability of the bamboo plant is the greatest danger to pandas, because it is the only food they eat.
- ☐ **C** pandas use bamboo sticks to defend themselves against other pandas.

2 'A panda research centre', is a place where people
- ☐ **A** look for pandas.
- ☐ **B** look after pandas.
- ☐ **C** study the panda.

3 'They can eat 4 kilos at a sitting', means the panda
- ☐ **A** can eat 4 kilos at one mealtime.
- ☐ **B** eats 4 kilos every time it sits down.
- ☐ **C** always eats 4 kilos at one mealtime.

4 'It was adopted as the symbol of the World Wildlife Fund', means
- ☐ **A** they decided to use a picture of a panda to represent their organization.
- ☐ **B** they decided to look after only giant pandas.
- ☐ **C** they keep one giant panda in a cage at their headquarters.

5 'The arrival of a panda at a zoo can turn a loss into a healthy profit', means that
- ☐ **A** a zoo which buys a panda can sell it for more than it paid.
- ☐ **B** more people pay to visit a zoo, and it stops losing money and starts making a good profit.
- ☐ **C** because more paying visitors come to the zoo, the zoo has more money to look after the animals' health, and can sell them for more money.

6 'About 1000 giant pandas still survive in the wild', means there are 1000 giant pandas and
- ☐ **A** they are all very savage.
- ☐ **B** their movements are controlled.
- ☐ **C** they still live outside zoos in their natural habitat.

7 'The panda regularly rates in the top ten of children's favourite animals', means
- ☐ **A** all children always vote for the panda as their favourite animal.
- ☐ **B** the panda is usually voted as one of the ten most popular animals by children.
- ☐ **C** children think that the panda is one of the ten most common animals in the world.

Exercise 2

Find words which mean:

1 a piece of metal or cloth, with a picture, design or lettering, which you can wear
2 a label which is stuck on a car
3 to join with others in giving money
4 to turn the body sideways from a lying position
5 to press with great force so there is breaking or injury
6 to move slowly pulling the body along the ground
7 often seen, well known
8 bad tempered and dangerous
9 hurt or injured by an animal
10 part of the body cut off

Unit 24

Language summary

Revision of Past Tenses — Question Tags

Exercise 1

'I still can't believe it happened. I drive a convertible MGB, and it was a scorching hot day so the roof was down. I had taken off my jacket, and put it on the passenger seat. Anyway, I was driving along Edgeware Road and I stopped at some traffic lights. I was sitting there, listening to the radio and waiting for the lights to change. Suddenly a young man reached over the side of the car, grabbed my jacket and disappeared into the crowd. The lights went green and all the cars behind me began blowing their horns. I just didn't know what to do! My wallet was in the inside jacket pocket, so was my cheque book . . . and my credit cards.'

Answer these questions.

1 What kind of car does he drive? ....

2 What was the weather like? ....

3 What had he done? ....

4 Where had he put his jacket? ....

5 Where was he driving? ....

6 Where did he stop? ....

7 What was he doing? ....

8 What did the young man do? ....

9 What did the other cars begin doing? ....

10 What was in his jacket? ....

Exercise 2

He parked on the pavement and phoned the police. A policeman arrived, and they went into a nearby coffee bar and sat down. He told the policeman what had happened. The policeman wrote it all down, and then checked through the statement.

The roof was down, *wasn't it?*

Write in the question tags.

1 You'd taken your jacket off,..

2 You'd put it on the passenger seat,..

3 You were driving along Edgeware Road,..

4 You stopped at the traffic lights,..

5 You were listening to the radio,..

6 You weren't looking at the street,..

7 He grabbed your jacket,..

8 You didn't see his face,..

9 He ran into the crowd,..

10 The other cars began blowing their horns,..

Exercise 3

It's a nice day, *isn't it?* It isn't a nice day, *is it?*

1 You aren't hungry,..

2 He smokes,..

3 You don't drive,..

4 She'd gone,..

5 He hasn't got a car,..

6 You'd rather play tennis,..

7 He'll see us later,..

8 You'd better not do it,..

9 There weren't enough tickets,..

10 He couldn't stop smoking,..

11 You've got enough,..

12 There was a lot,..

13 You won't tell anybody,..

14 I'm not late,..

15 They all speak English,..

16 You're supposed to be helping,..

17 You'd rather not play,..

18 They'd prefer to stay in,..

Unit 25

Language summary

Could	*it*	*have been*	*him?* *her?* *them?*

Could	*he* *she* *they*	*have*	*done it?* *killed him?* *shot him?*

It	*must* *could* *may (not)* *might (not)* *can't* *couldn't*	*have been*	*him.* *her.* *them.*

He *She* *They*	*must* *could* *may (not)* *might (not)* *can't* *couldn't*	*have*	*done it.* *killed him.* *shot him.*

Exercise 1

Five years ago, Larry Wallace was very poor. Now he's a millionaire.

He must have been very lucky.
He might have married a rich woman.
He may have been successful in business.
He could have robbed a bank.
or something else ...

Make sentences about each of these situations.

1 The door was locked, but the thief managed to get into the hotel room. ....

....

2 Mr and Mrs Sullivan are very worried. Their daughter, Judith, usually gets home from school at 4.30. It's 6 o'clock and she hasn't arrived yet. ....

....

3 Neil phoned his boss at 9 o'clock and said he was too ill to come to work. At 9.30 his boss phoned Neil's house, and there was no reply. ....

....

4 Gregg made a date with Penny. They arranged to meet outside the cinema at 7.30. It's 8 o'clock and she hasn't turned up. ....

....

5 Bob Cole escaped from prison. The police checked all the airports and ports, but they weren't able to find him. ....

....

6 Jake Rowley robbed a bank, hijacked a plane and parachuted out over the Amazon jungle. He's never been seen since. ....

....

7 The Lanstable painting 'Norfolk Sunset' which was stolen two years ago is still missing. It is so famous that it is impossible to sell. ....

....

8 A month ago, Tina was 10 kilos overweight. Now she's normal. ....

....

9 Five years ago, Francis Wright was a millionaire. Now he's penniless. ....

....

10 A woman has just wandered into a London police station. She has no documents or identification, but is wearing good clothes. She's lost her memory. ....

....

11 Terry Singleton was shipwrecked, and survived on a desert island alone for two years before he was rescued. ....

....

12 Daisy Armfield was on television last night. She said she was born in 1870. ....

....

13 Sam can't stop laughing. ....

....

14 Elizabeth has just read a letter, and she's crying. ....

....

15 At 5 o'clock in the morning, on an empty motorway, a car crashed into a bridge at 170 k.p.h. The driver was killed. ....

....

16 Valerie Simpson has just been sent to prison for thirty-five years. ....

....

17 The Queen has just given Herbert Thomas a medal for bravery. ....

....

18 A woman has just run into the street, screaming. ....

....

19 Someone on the radio said that he had seen a man 3 metres tall. ....

....

Unit 26

Look at this letter.

Mistral Foods Ltd.,
Fernwood Trading Estat
Warrington,
Lancs.

55, Willow Way,
Scarborough,
Yorkshire.
8th March 1983.

Dear Sirs,

I purchased a tin of 'Mistral Baked Beans in Tomato Sauce' a few days ago. I enclose the label. When I put the beans in a saucepan, I noticed a piece of glass, which is also enclosed. I was very angry. I could have cut my mouth or broken a tooth. I might even have given it to my small son. He might have swallowed it! I expect to hear from you.

Yours faithfully,
William Hind.

Exercise 1

Randolph Cooper lives at 22 Greenwood Avenue, Nottingham. He had just bought a second-hand car. It was a Calypso, registration CRA 749S. It had a one year guarantee. Just after he left the garage the brakes failed on a steep hill. He couldn't stop, and just missed a bus queue outside the school. He then hit a police car. Fortunately, he was unhurt.

Write a letter to the garage. Say what happened and what might have happened.

Exercise 2

Look at these notes.
Mrs Campbell, 17 Hodder Road, Kendal, Cumbria. Gas fitter/install new gas cooker. She/go to work. Told fitter/ let himself out when/finished. Came back/6 o'clock. House/ full of gas. She/heavy smoker. Luckily/not smoking.

Write a letter to the Gas Consumers' Council. Say what happened, and what might have happened.

Exercise 3

Look at these notes.
Mrs Wade, 83 years old. 62 Park Road, Eastleigh, Hants. Queuing/last bus. Last in queue. Bus came. Driver/ everybody/hurry. She/getting on/bus/pulled away. Almost fell off. Fortunately/let go of bar. Not hurt. Had to take/taxi home.

Write to the Hampshire Bus Company. Explain what happened. Say what might have happened.

Exercise 4

Have you ever found anything in a tin or packet? Have you ever had an accident? nearly had an accident? hurt yourself because of someone else's negligence?

Write a letter saying what happened and what might have happened.

Unit 27

Language summary

He	should shouldn't ought (not) to	have done it.

Exercise 1

Mr and Mrs Downes booked a holiday with Sunshine Tours. It was disastrous. When they got back, Mr Downes went to see the travel agent.

The plane didn't take off on time.
It should have taken off on time.

What else should have happened? Write your answers.

1 They didn't give us a meal on the plane.
2 The representative didn't meet us at the airport.
3 You hadn't sent the reservation to the hotel.

4 There were no rooms for us at the hotel.
5 They didn't find us another hotel.
6 They didn't apologize.

Exercise 2

Andrew Kerr lost his driving licence last month. In court, the police read out all the things he had done.

He reversed into a main road.
He shouldn't have reversed into a main road.

What else shouldn't he have done? Write your answers.

1 He forgot to indicate.
2 He drove too fast.
3 He went through a red light.
4 He had his arm round his girlfriend.
5 He hit a lamp-post.
6 He had drunk six whiskies.

Exercise 3

The headmaster of her son's school has just telephoned Mrs Raleigh to complain about her son's behaviour.

He didn't pay attention in class.
He ought to have paid attention in class.
He chewed gum during the music lesson.
He ought not to have chewed gum in the music lesson.

What other complaints did he make? Write your answers.

1 He wrote rude words on the blackboard.
2 He didn't do any homework last week.
3 He didn't learn his French irregular verbs.
4 He threw a book at another boy.
5 He didn't bring a pen to school.
6 He rode his bicycle in the school garden.
7 He didn't wear his uniform to school.
8 He didn't come to see me yesterday.
9 He was late every day last week.
10 He brought a dog into the classroom.

Exercise 4

Look at this letter of complaint, and write a reply from the company.

193, Winston Lane,
Tadworth.

27th August

The Complaints Dept,
T. Green Electrical,
Voltaire House,
Thorn Street,
Croydon.

Dear Sir,

I bought a hair-dryer at your branch in "The Tadworth Centre" shopping precinct last week. I'm afraid I didn't keep the receipt, and I threw away the box and the guarantee. When I opened the box I found it was the wrong colour. I had asked for pink and it was blue. I didn't take it back to the shop because I was too busy. I didn't even have time to phone the manager. I decided to keep it. When I plugged it in, it blew up. The switch was on 110 volts, and it should have been on 240 volts. Anyway, the dryer is now completely useless. I am not sending it to you, as postage is too expensive. The manager refused to exchange it and was very rude. Please refund my £13.50.

Yours faithfully,

Sandra Douglas

Unit 28 (Revision)

Language summary

Someone did it . . . it was done.	*Someone was doing it . . . it was being done.*	*Someone had done it . . .*
Someone did them . . . they were done.	*Someone was doing them . . . they were being done.*	*it had been done.*

Exercise 1

Complete this table.

-an/-ian		-ish		-ese	
Algeria	*Algerian*	Denmark	*Danish*	Sudan	*Sudanese*
Argentina	....	Finland	....	Senegal	....
Austria	....	Ireland	....	Portugal	....
Belgium	....	Poland	....	Japan	....
Brazil	....	Sweden	....	Burma	....
Canada	....	Turkey	....	China	....
Egypt	....	Britain	....	Lebanon	....
Hungary	....	England	....	Malta	....
Germany	....	Scotland	....	Nepal	....
India	....	Spain	....	Vietnam	....
Mexico	....				
Soviet Union	....				
United States	....				

others				-i	
Czechoslovakia	*Czech*	The Netherlands	....	Pakistan	*Pakistani*
France	....	Switzerland	....	Iraq	....
Greece	....	Thailand	....	Kuwait	....
Iceland	....	Wales	....	Yemen	....

Exercise 2

'Someone gave me a present.'
You can say **A** *'I was given a present.'*
B *'A present was given to me.'*
'I was given a present.' is more usual.

Change these sentences in both ways.

1 The boss promised them an increase in salary.
2 The company had offered her a good job.
3 His father had left him a fortune.
4 They sent me a telegram.
5 Someone had given them a map of the area.
6 Someone showed her the new house.

Exercise 3

Dorothy Booker was born in a small village near London. She moved when she was a child. The village has become a 'new town' and when she returned recently, everything had changed. The whole area looked like a building site!

They were building new houses.
New houses were being built.

Continue.

1 They were constructing a new shopping centre.
2 They were planting trees everywhere.
3 They were constructing roads.
4 They were building a school.
5 They were demolishing old houses.

Exercise 4

Rudi was played by Joe Revolta.

Write twelve more sentences.

★ SLASH! NEW ROCK MUSICAL ★
*Producer BOB STALEWOOD
*Director CHARLES ORSON
*Screenplay TOM ALLEN
From an original story by TRUMAN HOOD
Music composed by HAZEL WILCOX
Performed by *THE FUZZ*
TITLE SONG *'SLASH'* sung by BUTCH LANG
Dance sequences choreographed by Sheila Darwin
Fight sequences arranged by Jerry Floyd
FEATURING
★ *JOE REVOLTA* as 'Rudi'
★ *CYNTHIA NEWTON* as 'Carmen'
Also starring *JASON DOUGLAS* as 'the Priest' and *MARIA MONTROSE* as 'Big Mama'

A FILM
TRANS-AMERICA CORP.

Unit 29

Language summary

They	must could may might might even couldn't can't	have been doing it.
	should shouldn't	

He killed himself <u>after throwing</u> the bodies into the sea.

Exercise 1

1 *He must have been drinking.* **2** .... **3** ....

4 .... **5** .... **6** ....

Exercise 2

What do you think these people were doing a short time ago?
Write sentences with: may/might/could have been (doing) . . .

1 A ....
B ....
C ....

2 A ....
B ....
C ....

3 A ....
B ....
C ....

continued

Exercise 3

Someone says 'I heard Maria speaking French.'
You know she doesn't speak French.
She couldn't have been speaking French.

1 The traffic policeman says 'You were doing 150 k.p.h.' You know the maximum speed of your car is 120 k.p.h.

....

....

2 Someone says 'I saw Jack sitting in a café.' You know he is out of town.

....

....

3 Someone says 'I saw Jane eating in the Steak House.' You know she's a vegetarian.

....

....

4 Someone says 'Our baby was reading Shakespeare!'

....

....

Exercise 4

She was smoking near the petrol pump. *She shouldn't have been smoking near the petrol pump.*

1 The night watchman was sleeping. ....

....

....

2 He was laughing during the funeral. ....

....

....

3 He was driving at 100 k.p.h. through the town centre ....

....

....

4 They were smoking while the plane was taking off. ....

....

....

Exercise 5

He was driving on the left in Germany when he crashed.
A *He shouldn't have been driving on the left.*
B *He should have been driving on the right.*

1 The student was sleeping during the lecture.

A ....

B ....

2 The footballer was arguing with the referee when the other team scored.

A ....

B ....

3 She was watching T.V. when the milk boiled over.

A ....

B ....

4 He was looking at a pretty girl when he walked into the lamp-post.

A ....

B ....

Exercise 6

He took his clothes off, then he jumped into the river. *He jumped into the river after taking his clothes off.*

1 First she wrote a suicide note, then she jumped out of the window.

....

....

2 He asked her to marry him, then he kissed her.

....

....

3 He saw the accident. He telephoned the police.

....

....

4 First she asked permission, then she went home.

....

....

Unit 30

Language summary

He *She* *They* *It*	*must* *could* *may* *might* *might even* *can't* *couldn't*	*be*	*crazy.* *at home.*
		be doing	*something.*
		have been done	
		have been doing	

Exercise 1

Write the correct names in the boxes on the picture. Tracy's the second from the left in the front row. Rod's behind her. You can see Joseph in the top right of the picture. Alice is between Joseph and Rod. Deborah's in the bottom left of the picture. Philip's in front of Joseph. Dean's the fourth from the right in the back row. Sally's the other.

Exercise 2

Look at the man in the bottom left corner.

He must be waiting to see the doctor. He must have broken his leg. He must have seen a doctor before, because his leg's in plaster. He might have been playing football when he broke it, or he might have been skiing. He might not be waiting to see the doctor about his leg. He might have something else wrong with him.

Write sentences about the other people in the waiting room.

1 The second person from the left. ...
2 The man with spots. ...
3 The woman in the corner. ...
4 The little boy standing in front of her. ...
5 The old man in the middle. ...
6 The woman next to him. ...
7 The man next to the door. ...
8 The woman on the right of the door. ...
9 The man next to her. ...
10 The man sitting opposite the pregnant lady. ...

Unit 31

Language summary

Sorry.
I'm (terribly) sorry.
I really am very sorry.
I'm ever so sorry.
I just want(ed) to apologize.

Don't worry about it.
It really doesn't matter.
Forget it.
(It's) all right.
It's nothing.
I don't want to hear any more about it.

I didn't mean to (do it).
I didn't realize (I had to do it).
It was so (silly) of me to (do it).
It won't happen again.
It wasn't my fault.
What more can I say?

Exercise

Look at these sentences.
Put the numbers in the appropriate spaces. Read all of the sentences carefully before you begin.

1 I'm terribly sorry, officer. I just didn't see the red light.
2 Yes, you're right. It was very careless of me. I'm sorry. I hope you're not hurt.
3 I must have dialled the wrong number. Sorry.
4 Is it? Oh, yes. I'm terribly sorry. It looks just like mine.
5 Oh, my God! Is it? I didn't realize. I thought it was the Gents. Sorry.
6 I am sorry. I am a foreigner. It won't happen again.
7 Really! I didn't know it was a private club. Sorry.
8 I'm awfully sorry. I thought you were someone else.
9 Oh, I'm ever so sorry. I didn't see you sitting there. It's so dark in here.
10 Of course it is. How silly of me! I don't usually forget names.
11 I'm awfully sorry. I thought they were all unreserved.
12 No, not this time. The alarm clock didn't go off. Sorry I'm late again. It won't happen again.
13 I really must apologize. I thought I had my wallet with me.
14 I'm sorry. I didn't mean to ignore you. I just didn't see you, that's all.
15 Yes, I know. I'm sorry but I lost your number.

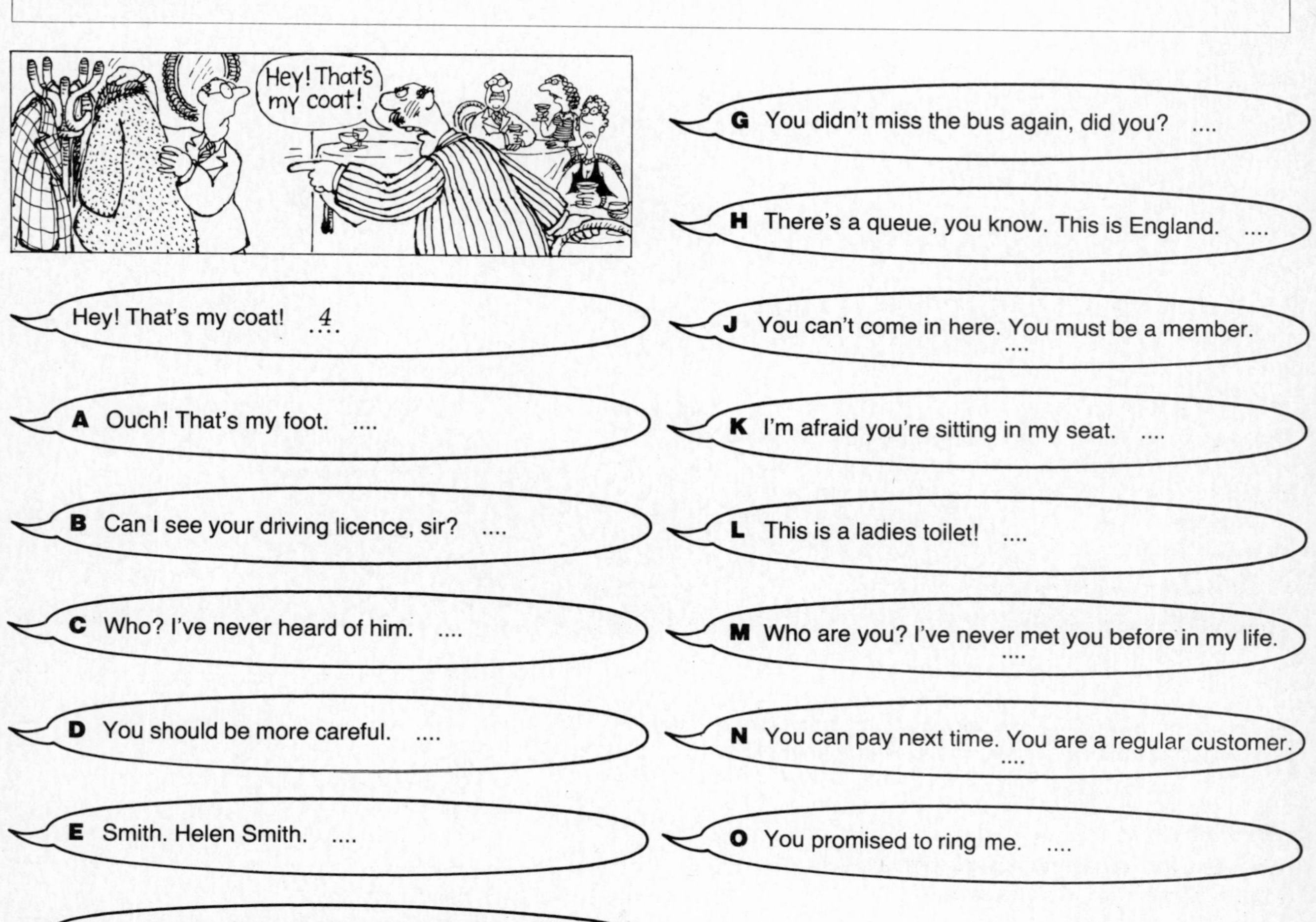

Unit 32

Language summary

Stop *Remember*	*doing*	contrasted with	*Stop* *Remember* *Forget*	*to do*

Exercise 1

Butcher's
Bank ✓
Baker's
Greengrocer's ✓
Post Office ✓
Dry-cleaner's
Chemist's ✓
Newsagent's
Florist's ✓
Toy shop ✓

Linda's in hospital. She's expecting her third baby. Her husband, Chris, is looking after the other two children. Linda gave him a shopping list. He didn't remember to get everything, but he did get some of the things.
He forgot to get some meat.
He remembered to get some money.

Write eight more sentences.

1 ....
2 ....
3 ....
4 ....
5 ....
6 ....
7 ....
8 ....

Exercise 2

He stopped at the bank to get some money.

Write five more sentences.

1 ....
2 ....
3 ....
4 ....
5 ....

Exercise 3

Ten years ago Patrick was a rich young man. He used to drink, smoke, gamble, eat in expensive restaurants and go out with beautiful women. Eight years ago everything changed. He joined a monastery and became a monk. His name is now Brother Anselm.

He stopped drinking eight years ago.

Write four more sentences.

1 ....
2 ....
3 ....
4 ....

Exercise 4

What can you remember doing in primary school?
I can remember listening to stories.
I remember learning to read.

Write four more sentences.

1 ....
2 ....
3 ....
4 ....

continued

Exercise 5

She was typing. The telephone rang, and she answered it.

A *She stopping typing.*
B *She stopped to answer the phone.*

1 The boys were playing football. Concorde flew over. Everybody looked up in the air.

A ....

B ....

....

2 He was driving along the motorway. He felt tired. He had a cup of coffee.

A ....

B ....

....

3 During the cricket match someone brought a tray of drinks onto the field for the players.

A ....

B ....

....

4 The teacher gave the students a five minute break.

A ....

B ....

....

5 In the middle of the concert, the guitarist had to change a string.

A ....

B ....

....

6 During the speech the politician had to blow his nose.

A ....

B ....

....

Exercise 6

WATCH OUT!
There's a thief about

When you are leaving your house to go on holiday, remember to

1. *lock all the doors*
2. *fasten all the windows*
3. *switch off the lights*
4. *close the gates*
5. *lock any ladders or tools in the garage*

WESSEX POLICE

Robert Mark is a very careful man. When he went on holiday recently, he remembered all the precautions.

He remembered to lock all the doors.

Write four more sentences.

1 ....

2 ....

3 ....

4 ....

Exercise 7

When he got back from his holiday, he was very worried because the gate was open, the bedroom window was open and his ladder was leaning against the wall. The front door was also open, and the lights were on in the hall. He was worried because he could remember closing the gate.

Write four more sentences.

1 ....

2 ....

3 ....

4 ....

Unit 33

Walt Disney

Walt Disney was born on 5th December, 1901, in Chicago. His father was Irish-Canadian, and his mother was German - American. Disney attended McKinley High School in Chicago, and left at the age of 17 to become an ambulance driver in the First World War. In 1919 he moved to Kansas City and became a commercial artist. He went to Hollywood in 1923 to become an animator, working on cartoon films. He was married in 1925 to Lillian Bounds. He drew the first Mickey Mouse cartoon in 1928. He was the first producer to use Technicolor, on 'Flowers and Trees' in 1933. By 1934 he employed a staff of 700. He created Donald Duck in 1936.

In 1937 he made the first full length cartoon feature film' Snow White and the Seven Dwarfs'.

Over the next thirty years he made a series of successful cartoon Films, including 'Pinocchio' (1939), 'Fantasia' (1940), 'Bambi' (1943), 'Lady and the Tramp' (1956), '101 Dalmations' (1956) and the posthumous 'The Jungle Book' (1967). His series of 'True Life Adventures', which were animal documentaries, were also very popular. His studio also made ordinary feature films for children, such as '20 000 Leagues Under the Sea'. In 1955 Disneyland was opened in California, and this was followed in 1971 by Disney World Florida. Disney died on December 15th, 1966 in Burbank, California, at the age of 65. His films are still shown regularly at the cinema, and because of their timeless quality, will continue to be shown for years to come.

Look at these notes on Disney.

WALTER ELIAS DISNEY 5/12/01 – 15/12/66. Born Chicago, Father: Irish–Canadian. Mother: German–American. McKinley High Sc., Chic. to 17. Then ambulance driver in WW1. 1919- Kansas City. Commercial Artist. 1923- Hollywood, animator, cartoon films. 1925- Married Lillian Bounds. 1928- 1st Mickey Mouse. 1933- 1st technicolour – 'Flowers & Trees'. 1934- staff of 700. 1936-'Donald Duck'. 1937- 1st full length cartoon feature film, 'Snow White and the 7 Dwarfs'. Next 30 years- films included 'Pinocchio' (39), 'Fantasia' (40), 'Bambi' (43), 'Lady & the Tramp' (56), '101 Dalmations' (56), + posthumous 'The Jungle Book' (67). Also 'True Life Adventures' (animal documentaries) – v. popular. + ordinary feature films for children – e.g. '20,000 Leagues Under The Sea'. 1955- Disneyland, Ca. 1971- Disney World, Fla. Died Burbank, Ca. Films still shown regularly – timeless quality. Will continue in future.

Exercise 1

Read these notes, and use them to write a short biography.

MARILYN MONROE 1/6/26 – 5/8/62. Real name: Norma Jean Baker. Born L.A., Ca. 1934- mother mentally ill. 1935 MM to L.A. orphanage. 1st married, age 16, 1942. Divorce, age 19. 1944- photographic model (calendars). Film career began 1948 'Dangerous Years'. 1st big success in 'Niagara', (52). Married U.S. baseball star, Joe di Maggio, (52). Films included 'Gentlemen Prefer Blondes' (53), 'How to Marry a Millionaire' (53), 'The Seven Year Itch' (55), 'Some Like It Hot' (59). Husband No. 3 Arthur Miller – U.S. playwright. He wrote last film 'The Misfits' (61). Found dead, Hollywood. Overdose of barbiturates. Verdict – suicide. Some questions in recent years about this. Sex symbol – but lonely, unhappy private life. Perhaps most of films not great movies – but MM symbolized Hollywood.

....

....

....

....

....

....

....

continued

Exercise 2

Read these short biographies of Ernest Hemingway and George Orwell.

Ernest Miller Hemingway was born in 1899. His father was a doctor and he was the second of six children. Their home was at Oak Park, a Chicago suburb.

In 1917 Hemingway joined the Kansas City *Star* as a cub reporter. The following year he volunteered to work as an ambulance driver on the Italian front where he was badly wounded but twice decorated for his services. He returned to America in 1919 and married in 1921. In 1922 he reported on the Greco-Turkish war then two years later resigned from journalism to devote himself to fiction. He settled in Paris where he renewed his earlier friendship with such fellow-American expatriates as Ezra Pound and Gertrude Stein. Their encouragement and criticism were to play a valuable part in the formation of his style.

Hemingway's first two published works were *Three Stories and Ten Poems* and *In Our Time* but it was the satirical novel, *The Torrents of Spring*, which established his name more widely. His international reputation was firmly secured by his next three books: *Fiesta*, *Men Without Women* and *A Farewell to Arms*.

He was passionately involved with bullfighting, big-game hunting and deep-sea fishing, and his writing reflected this. He visited Spain during the Civil War and described his experiences in the bestseller, *For Whom the Bell Tolls*. His direct and deceptively simple style of writing spawned generations of imitators but no equals. Recognition of his position in contemporary literature came in 1954 when he was awarded the Nobel Prize, following the publication of *The Old Man and the Sea*. Ernest Hemingway died in 1961.

From the introduction to the Panther edition of *Torrents of Spring.*

Eric Arthur Blair (George Orwell) was born in 1903 in India, where his father worked for the Civil Service. The family moved to England in 1907 and in 1917 Orwell entered Eton, where he contributed regularly to the various college magazines. He left in 1921 and joined the Indian Imperial Police in Burma the following year, in which he served until 1928.

His first published article appeared in *Le Monde* in October 1928, while Orwell was living in Paris, and he returned to England in 1929 to take up work as a private tutor and later as a schoolteacher (1932). *Down and Out in Paris and London* was published in 1933. Due to his poor health, Orwell gave up teaching and worked as a part-time assistant in a Hampstead bookshop, and later was able to earn his living reviewing novels for the *New English Weekly*, a post he kept until 1940.

At the end of 1936 Orwell went to Spain in the Civil War and was wounded. During the Second World War he was a member of the Home Guard and worked for the BBC Eastern Service from 1940 to 1943. As literary editor of *Tribune* he contributed a regular page of political and literary commentary. From 1945 Orwell was the *Observer's* war correspondent and later became a regular contributor to the *Manchester Evening News.*

Orwell suffered from tuberculosis, and was in and out of hospital from 1947 until his death in 1950. He was forty-six.

His publications include *The Road to Wigan Pier, Coming Up for Air, Keep the Aspridistra Flying* and *Homage to Catalonia.* Orwell's name became widely known with the publication of *Animal Farm* and *Nineteen Eighty-Four,* both of which have sold more than two million copies. All Orwell's works have been published in Penguins.

From the introduction to the Penguin edition of *Down and out in Paris and London.*

Make notes on Hemingway using these headings.

Full name ....

Born (Where? When?) ....

....

Family ....

Early career ....

....

Travel ....

....

Achievements ....

....

....

....

Interests ....

....

Awards ....

Death ....

Exercise 3

Read the notes on Walt Disney and Marilyn Monroe. Make similar notes on George Orwell.

....

....

....

....

....

....

....

Unit 34

Language summary

If you do this, I'll do that.
If you don't do this, I'll do that.
Unless you do this, I'll do that.

Look at these car hire rates.

Hertz® LOCAL RATES PROVINCES

GROUP	CAR	DAILY INC. 200 MILES 2 DAYS + PER DAY UNLIMITED	WEEKLY UNLIMITED	EXCESS MILES PER MILE
	MANUAL TRANSMISSION			
A	**FORD** Fiesta 1.1L MINI METRO 1.0L or similar	£15.00	£84.00	12p
B	**FORD** Escort 1.3L (5 door) or similar	£16.50	£91.00	14p
C	**FORD** Cortina 1.6L CAVALIER 1.6L	£18.50	£105.00	15p
	AUTOMATIC TRANSMISSION			
F	**FORD** Cortina 2.0GL or similar SAAB 900 GLE/S	£31.00	£161.00	22p
	ESTATE CARS			
I	**FORD** Cortina 1.6L (Manual) or similar	£25.00	£126.00	19p

Exercise 1

Mrs Davies wants to rent a car for the day.

A *If she rents a Ford Fiesta, it'll cost £15.00 per day.*
B *If she drives more than 200 miles, she'll have to pay 12p per mile extra.*

Write two sentences about each of these cars: Ford Escort 1.3L/Cavalier/Saab 900GLE/Ford Cortina 1.6L Estate.

Exercise 2

If she rents a Mini-Metro for 5 days, it will cost £75·00.

Write sentences.

1. Ford Cortina 1.0GL/the weekend.
2. Cavalier/2 days.
3. Ford Cortina Estate/a week.
4. Ford Escort/3 days.

Exercise 3

If she wants a 5-door car, she'll rent an Escort.

Write sentences.

1. They/small cheap car.
2. He/automatic.
3. You/Estate.

Exercise 4

A *How much will it be if we rent a Fiesta for a week?*
B *A Fiesta? Let me see . . . that'll be £84.00.*

Ask and answer about the other cars for different periods of time.

Exercise 5

It's half-time in a very important football match. The score is Kings Park Rovers 3, Eastfield United 0. Brian Huff, the Eastfield manager has just walked into the dressing room. He's furious! He's made some notes.

Unless we win this match, I'll resign!

Write six more sentences.

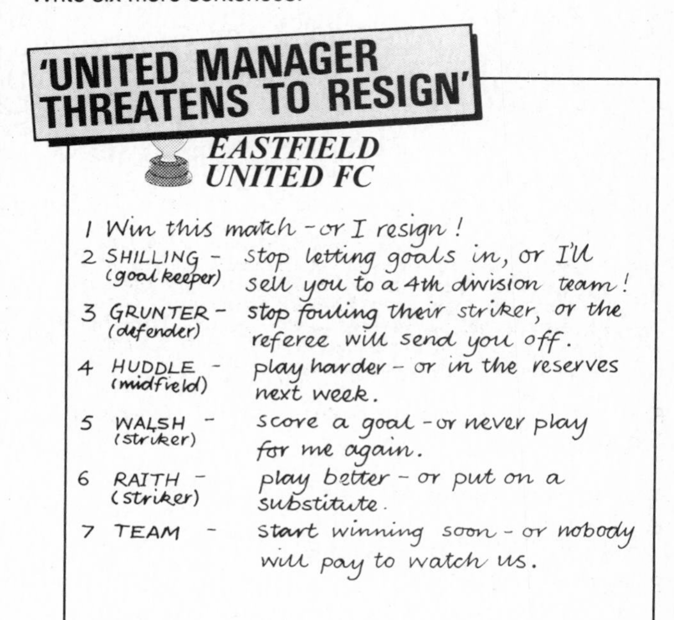

Exercise 6

If we don't win this match, I'll resign!

Write six more sentences.

Exercise 7

Put 'if' or 'unless' into the spaces in these sentences.

1. .... we hurry, we'll miss the bus.
2. Will you phone me, ... you come to England?
3. .... you see Jane, ask her to contact me.
4. You'll never pass your exam, ... you don't work harder.
5. Eastfield won't win .... they begin playing better.
6. .... you forget our address, you can find it in the phone book.
7. You won't pass your driving test, ... you drive more carefully.
8. He'll be ill .... he doesn't stop worrying so much.
9. We'll go to the beach tomorrow .... it's raining.
10. We'll never get there on time .... the train leaves soon.

Unit 35

Language summary

If you did this, I'd do that.
If you did(n't do) this, I would(n't) do that.
Unless you did this, I would(n't) do that.

If you do this, I'll do that.
If you did this, I'd do that.

Look at this.

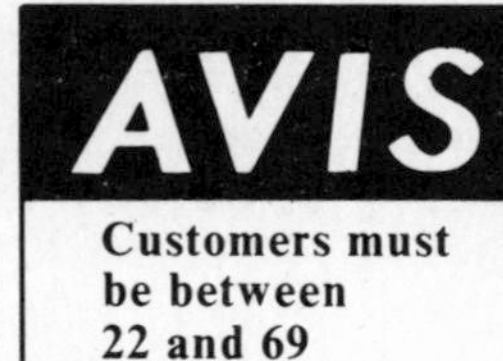

Exercise 1

I'm sorry. If you haven't got a ticket, you can't see the game.

Write four more sentences.

Exercise 2

You can't see the game unless you've got a ticket.

Write four more sentences.

Exercise 3

I want to see the game, but I haven't got a ticket. *If I had a ticket, I could see the game.*

1 He'd love to see the film, but he's only 13 and he's not with an adult.

....

....

2 She's nearly run out of petrol. She's got a cheque book, but no cash.

....

....

3 They'd like to rent a car, but he's only 20, and so is she.

....

....

4 I'd like to borrow some money, but I don't own a house.

....

....

Exercise 4

Put 'if' or 'unless' into the spaces in these sentences.

1 I wouldn't buy it .... it had a guarantee.

2 .... I were you, I'd see a doctor about that cough.

3 Who would you ask .... you didn't know how to do it?

4 I'd buy it .... I could afford it.

5 I wouldn't buy it .... I could afford it.

6 I would refuse to go .... they paid my expenses.

7 She's very lazy. She'd pass .... she tried harder.

8 He wouldn't be able to go .... we could find a baby-sitter

9 He wouldn't spend all that money .... he weren't very rich.

10 I don't agree with his economic policy. I wouldn't vote for him .... he changed it.

Exercise 5

Darren Shaw's 18. He's just been to see his girlfriend's father, Colonel Smythe-Fortescue. He wants to marry Fiona, the Colonel's 16-year-old daughter. This is what the Colonel said.

'There are just one or two conditions, young man. Get some qualifications, get a job, save some money. Find a place to live, sell that noisy motor-cycle, stop smoking, stop drinking, cut your hair, remove those tattoos from your arms . . . and remove that earring from your ear. When you've done all these things, we might discuss it again.'

'I don't understand . . .' Darren said.

'Well,' said the Colonel, *'I wouldn't let you marry her unless you had some qualifications.'*

Write nine more sentences with 'unless'.

Unit 36

Questionnaire: **HOW AGGRESSIVE ARE YOU ?**

1 If your car were stuck in a traffic jam, would you :

A ☐ bang your horn, and curse the Minister of Transport ?
B ☐ turn on the car radio, and relax ?
C ☐ feel slightly annoyed, but resign yourself to the situation ?

2 If you could have a new car, would you prefer to have :

A ☐ a comfortable, luxury saloon ?
B ☐ an uncomfortable but fast sports car ?
C ☐ an economical, easy-to-park small car ?

3 If you were watching T.V., which of these would you choose :

A ☐ a western ?
B ☐ a romantic comedy ?
C ☐ a boxing match ?

4 If you were getting on a bus, and there were only one seat left, would you:

A ☐ rush to get it ?
B ☐ look to see if there were anyone older who might want it ?
C ☐ make no special effort to get there first ?

5 If you were at a party and your boyfriend / girlfriend were surrounded by members of the opposite sex who found him / her attractive, would you :

A ☐ grab his / her arm and leave the party ?
B ☐ feel happy because he / she was having a good time ?
C ☐ go over, put your arm round him / her and join the conversation ?

6 Do you own any of these (or would you like to) ?

A ☐ an Alsatian dog
B ☐ a fast car or motor-cycle
C ☐ a weapon of any kind
D ☐ a prize for winning a sports event
E ☐ books about war
F ☐ any kind of uniform

7 A man has killed a child. Should he be :

A ☐ hanged ?
B ☐ imprisoned for life ?
C ☐ sent for psychiatric treatment ?

8 Have you been in a public argument (or fight) during the last two years ?

A ☐ often
B ☐ once or twice
C ☐ never

9 You have just had an argument with a friend. Would you say :

A ☐ "I won't speak to him / her, unless he / she apologizes to me."
B ☐ "I'd better phone him / her and apologise."
C ☐ "I think I'll wait and see what happens."

10 Which of these statements is true for you ?

A ☐ "I would never hit anybody unless they hit me first."
B ☐ "I would never hit anybody for any reason."
C ☐ "I would never hit anybody unless I were very angry."

What did you score ?

1 A.3 B.0 C.1
2 A.1 B.3 C.0
3 A.1 B.0 C.3
4 A.3 B.0 C.0
5 A.3 B.0 C.2
6 Score 1 for each that you have, or would like to have.
7 A.3 B.1 C.0
8 A.3 B.1 C.0
9 A.3 B.0 C.1
10 A.1 B.0 C.4

Results
19–34 You are a fairly aggressive person. I wouldn't like to step on your foot !
7–18 You are a fairly balanced person.
0–6 You may be too placid. Remember that a little aggression is normal.

Exercise 1

Go through the questionnaire and work out your score.

Exercise 2

Ask another student the questions and work out his/her score.

Exercise 3

If my car were stuck in a traffic jam, I'd be very angry, but I wouldn't bang my horn.

Use your results to write out nine sentences.

Exercise 4

Look at the scores. Do you agree with them? Why/why not? Discuss.

Unit 37

Language summary

Would you have said anything?	*I*	*'d*	*have*	*said*	*something*
What would you have done?		*would*		*done*	
		wouldn't			*anything*

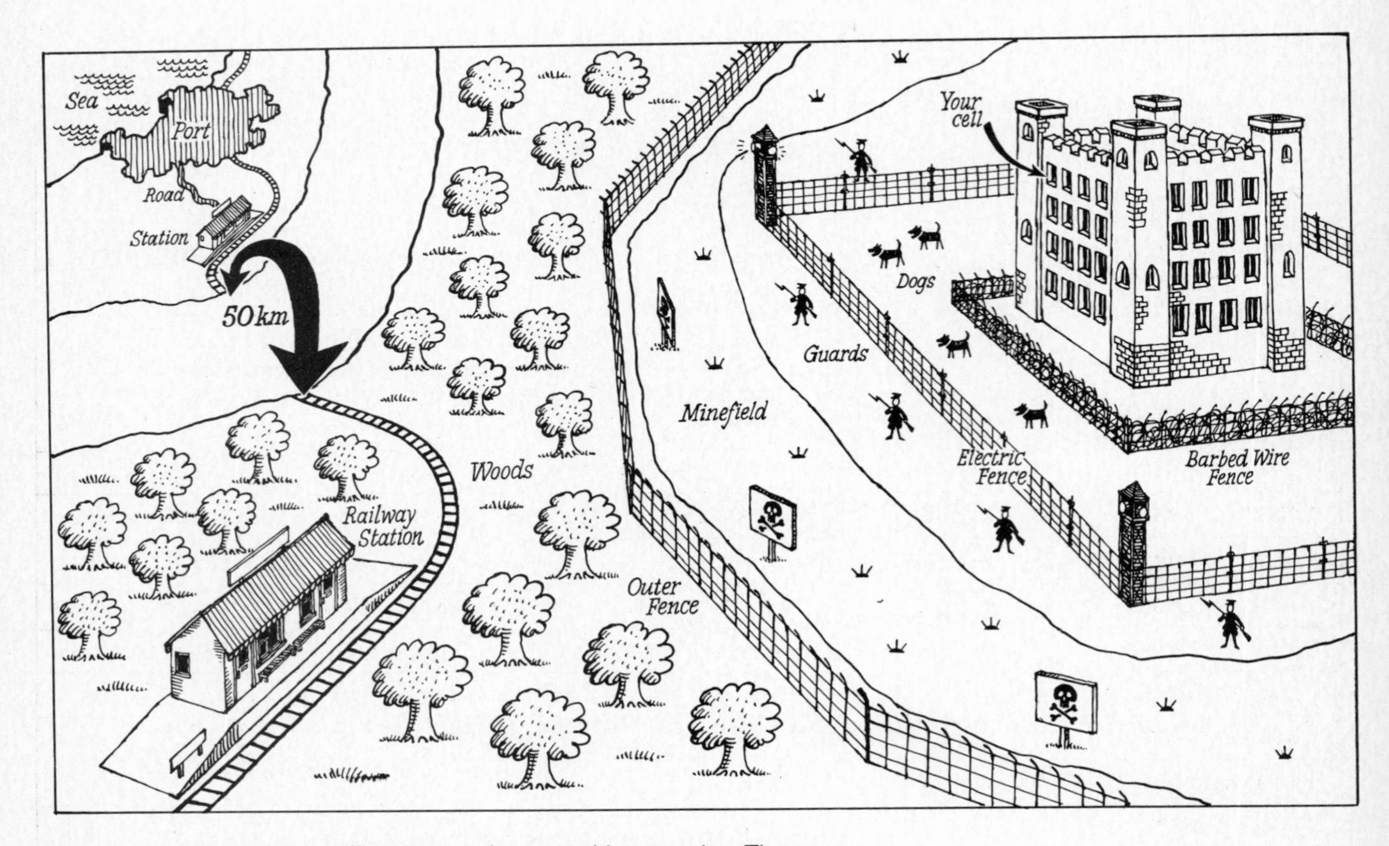

At an army college trainee officers were given a problem to solve. They were shown a map of a prisoner-of-war camp. They had to imagine that they were prisoners in the camp. They had some vital information, so it was very important for them to escape. Secret agents couldn't get them out, but they could arrange to leave some things to help the prisoners to escape. The officers had to say how they would have escaped, and what they would have done at each obstacle. Look at the plan of the prison camp, look at the notes and say what you would have done.

This is what the secret agents provided for the escape.

1 cell, window bars – hacksaw/dynamite.
2 cell – ground – rope/a large balloon.
3 barbed wire fence – a ladder/wire cutters.
4 dogs – tranquillizers/a knife.
5 electric fence – wire cutters/a spade.
6 guards – a spare uniform/a gun.
7 minefield – an accurate map/a metal detector.
8 outer fence – a pile of bricks/a long wooden pole.
9 near railway station – a phrase book/a sign saying 'deaf & dumb'.
10 next station – a car/a bicycle.
11 port – a rowing boat/seaman's papers from a neutral country.

Exercise 1

cell, window bars – a hacksaw/dynamite.
I could have used the jacksaw or the dynamite.

Write ten more sentences.

Exercise 2

I would have sawn through the bars.

Write ten more sentences.

Exercise 3

Why wouldn't you have used the dynamite?
Because it would have made too much noise.

Write ten more questions and answers.

Exercise 4

Write a paragraph and describe how you would have escaped, and why you would have chosen this method.

Unit 38

Language summary

If	I / he / she / we / you / they	'd / had / hadn't / had not	done that, / seen that, / been there,	I / he / she / we / you / they	'd / would / wouldn't / would not	've / have	done that. / seen this. / known this.

Look at this.

St. Bernard's Hospital
CASTERBRIDGE

Casualty department — Daily report — 16 September

PATIENT	AGE	INJURY	CAUSE
PAUL COOK	2	minor burns to hands	fire without a guard
SARAH DEAN	4	scalded face & neck	pulled pan of boiling milk from cooker- no pan guards
MARK WILSON	3½	drank bleach	not on high shelf
ERNEST SMITH	72	electric shock	bare wires near plug
ERIC CLARKE	48	broken collar-bone	fell off ladder - nobody holding the bottom
EMMA AUSTEN	10 mths	bruises	fell downstairs - no gate on stairs
DAPHNE WOODS	31	deep cuts to arms & legs	walked through glass door - not safety glass
CLAIRE GREEN	18 mths	ate 20 vitamin pills	pills not in a cupboard with a lock
JASON ADAMS	5	cut finger	mother left scissors on the floor
FLORENCE HOPE	81	severe burns	nightdress caught fire - mirror over fireplace
DIANA FORD	40	lost half her hair	hair caught in factory machine - not wearing hat
ANN BLAKE	18	broken leg	car reversed into her - driver didn't look in mirror
DAVID CASEY	26	broken ribs	car crashed - drank too much

Exercise 1

If the fire had had a guard, Paul wouldn't have burnt his hands.

Write twelve more sentences.

Exercise 2

Look at these newspaper headlines.

TRAIN CRASH- Driver failed to stop at SIGNAL

DISCO FIRE - 4 KILLED EMERGENCY EXIT CLOSED

Yacht Sinks- CREW IGNORED STORM WARNING

GARAGE BURNT TO THE GROUND- LIGHTED CIGARETTE LEFT IN WASTE-BIN

PLANE CRASH- pilot misunderstood air traffic control

Boy shoots baby brother- FATHER LEFT LOADED GUN IN DRAWER

CYCLIST KILLED- No lights on bicycle

The train wouldn't have crashed | *if the driver hadn't failed to stop at the signal.*
if the driver had stopped at the signal.

Look at the headlines and write six more sentences.

Unit 39

The disagreeable manservant, whom I had hoped never to see again, opened the door. There were five expensive cars lounging in the drive, two of them with chauffeurs, and I thought that he looked at my little Fiat 500 with disdain. Then he looked at my suit and I could see that his eyebrows went up. 'What name?' he asked, though I felt sure that he remembered it well enough. He spoke in English with a bit of a cockney twang. So he had remembered my nationality.
'Jones,' I said.
'Doctor Fischer's engaged.'
'He's expecting me,' I said.
'Doctor Fischer's dining with friends.'
'I happen to be dining with him myself.'
'Have you an invitation?'
'Of course I have an invitation.'
'Let me see the card.'
'You can't. I left it at home.'
He scowled at me, but he wasn't confident - I could tell that. I said, 'I don't think Doctor Fischer would be very pleased if there's an empty place at his table. You'd better go and ask him.'
'What did you say your name was?'
'Jones.'
'Follow me.'
I followed his white coat through the hall and up the stairs. On the landing he turned to me. He said, 'If you've been lying to me...If you weren't invited...' He made a motion with his fists like a boxer sparring.
'What's your name?' I asked.
'What's that to do with you?'
'I just want to tell the Doctor how you welcome his friends.'
'Friends,' he said. 'He has no friends. I tell you, if you weren't invited...'
'I am invited.'
We turned the opposite way from the study where I had last seen Doctor Fischer and he flung open a door. 'Mr Jones,' the man grunted and I walked in, and there stood all the Toads looking at me. The men wore dinner jackets and Mrs Montgomery a long dress.
'Come in, Jones,' Doctor Fischer said. 'You can serve dinner as soon as it's ready, Albert.'
The table was laid with crystal glasses which caught the lights of a chandelier overhead: even the soup plates looked expensive. I wondered a little at seeing them there: it was hardly the season for cold soup. 'This is Jones, my son-in-law,' Doctor Fischer said. 'You must excuse his glove. It covers a deformity.'

From *Dr Fischer of Geneva, or the Bomb Party*, by Graham Greene. Penguin, 1981.

Exercise 1

Find words which mean:

1 having dinner
2 a room used for reading or writing
3 part of the body unnaturally or badly shaped
4 unpleasant and unfriendly
5 spoke in a low, rough way
6 opened quickly and forcibly
7 private road to a house
8 a branched, ornamental holder for lights hanging from the ceiling
9 space or passage at the top of a set of stairs from which one enters rooms
10 looked in a bad-tempered way

Exercise 2

1 'Doctor Fischer's engaged,' means
☐ **A** he is going to get married.
☐ **B** he is busy, so he can't see you.
☐ **C** he's in the toilet.

2 'He wasn't confident – I could tell that', means
☐ **A** I told him that he wasn't sure of himself.
☐ **B** I knew that he didn't know my secret.
☐ **C** I saw that he wasn't sure of himself.

3 'He spoke in English with a bit of a cockney twang', means
☐ **A** he usually spoke English to someone from London.
☐ **B** he spoke with a slight working-class London accent.
☐ **C** he spoke English ungrammatically.

4 'He made a motion with his fists like a boxer sparring', means
☐ **A** he closed his hands and waved them in a threatening way.
☐ **B** he tried to hit me, but just missed.
☐ **C** he hit me.

5 'There stood all the Toads looking at me', Jones says this because
☐ **A** Mr and Mrs Toad and their children were there.
☐ **B** There were several frog-like amphibious creatures. which would be served for dinner.
☐ **C** He had given the nickname 'toads' to this group of people because he disliked them.

6 'He looked at my little Fiat 500 with disdain', means
☐ **A** he was jealous because I owned a car.
☐ **B** he was surprised to see such a small car.
☐ **C** he thought my car was worthless and out-of-place.

Exercise 3

How might the manservant have finished these sentences?

'If you've been lying to me, I'll ....'

'If you weren't invited, I'd ....'

Unit 40

Language summary

<u>Unless</u> you'd studied film history, you would never have heard of them.
We'd never have gone fly-drive <u>unless</u> we'd had the kids with us.
<u>If only</u> (we'd had our grandchildren with us!)

Exercise 1

Look at the example, and complete the table.

I'll do it if I have the time.	*I would do it if I had the time.*	*I would have done it if I had had the time.*
If I see her, I'll tell her.	....	....
If she doesn't try, she won't succeed.	....	....
Will you do it if I ask you?	....	....
....	I'd buy it if you gave me a discount.	....
....	....	If I had been ill, I would have stayed at home.
....	If I knew the answer, I would tell him.	....
What will you do if the bus doesn't come?	....	....
....	....	I would have been sorry if she had left.
....	I wouldn't stay in this job if I could find another one.	....
....	They would get wet if it rained.	....
....	....	Would he have passed if he had studied hard?
It won't bite you unless you move.	....	....

continued

....	....	We wouldn't have gone out unless it had stopped snowing.
....	He wouldn't marry her unless she were rich.	....
Will you pay him if he does it?	....	....

Exercise 2

Complete these sentences.

1. He wouldn't have jumped if ....
2. You'll never learn English unless ....
3. If you don't stop smoking ....
4. If you go to the casino ....
5. If I were Prime Minister ....
6. If I could go anywhere in the world ....
7. I would never forgive you if ....
8. If I'd seen the price ticket ....
9. I wouldn't have lent him the money if ....
10. If you don't practise ....
11. I'll kill you if ....
12. Unless it's a nice day ....
13. She wouldn't have bought it unless ....
14. If he'd known the police car was behind him ....
15. She wouldn't have married him unless ....
16. You would earn more money if ....
17. I wouldn't go unless ....
18. I wouldn't have believed him if ....
19. If I had three months holiday ....
20. I wouldn't have done this exercise unless ....

Revision

Read through Units 1–40 in the Student's book, and answer these questions.

Unit

1 What does John Benson do? ....

2 What will Jason be doing at 8 o'clock? ....

3 Where and when was Jason born? ....

4 How far will each competitor have driven by Thursday night? ....

5 What has George given up doing? ....

6 How should you apply for the job at Fernside Engineering? ....

7 What have the Council promised to give Mrs Hamilton? ....

8 Why didn't Mr Brown go to Albert Harper's funeral? ....

9 What has Barbara forbidden the children to do? ....

10 What did he pretend to do after the man took a second biscuit? ....

11 The man wearing a bow tie asked two questions. What was the second? ....

12 Why will Norman need some small change? ....

13 How long will Norman be staying in Spain? ....

14 What is 'the yen'? ....

15 What does a pickpocket do? ....

16 What wouldn't they let him photograph? ....

17 Does Lisa prefer navy blue or black? ....

18 What does Bert Woods think the police ought to do? ....

19 How many times did the wheels hit the runway? ....

20 Why did Justin offer so much money for the painting? ....

21 What does Sidney think Mr Sykes might be doing in the garden? ....

22 What was Smith supposed to be doing? ....

23 How does the lemming commit 'suicide'? ....

24 Why was Tristan arrested last year? ....

25 Who do you think killed Lord Gurney? ....

26 Why should you keep any receipts you are given? ....

27 What should the customer have read? ....

28 What was the harmonium used for? ....

29 Why does Mark say, 'They must have been eating?' ....

30 How do you think the house got onto the truck? ....

31 How did Sharon apologize for being late? ....

32 What did Stan stop to do at Burnham Wood? ....

33 Where was the Beatles' last performance? ....

34 Why must he pay the ransom money? ....

35 Tina wouldn't take the job in New York unless she were offered three things. What are they? ....

36 What could terrorists do if they captured a reactor? ....

37 What would you have done if you had been in Mr Horniman's situation? ....

38 What might have happened if Mrs Lewis hadn't noticed Debbie's mistake? ....

39 Why does Maurice know every flower and tree in the garden? ....

40 Why were Matthew and Polly pleased that there was a T.V. in the hotel room? ....